# Student's Solutions Manual

to accompany

# Elementary Statistics
## A Brief Version

## Fourth Edition

**Allan G. Bluman**
*Professor Emeritus*
*Community College of Allegheny County*

Prepared by
**Sally Robinson**
*South Plains College*

 **Higher Education**

Boston   Burr Ridge, IL   Dubuque, IA   New York   San Francisco   St. Louis
Bangkok   Bogotá   Caracas   Kuala Lumpur   Lisbon   London   Madrid   Mexico City
Milan   Montreal   New Delhi   Santiago   Seoul   Singapore   Sydney   Taipei   Toronto

**The McGraw·Hill Companies**

Student's Solutions Manual to accompany
ELEMENTARY STATISTICS: A BRIEF VERSION, FOURTH EDITION
ALLAN G. BLUMAN

Published by McGraw-Hill Higher Education, an imprint of The McGraw-Hill Companies, Inc., 1221 Avenue of the Americas, New York, NY 10020. Copyright © 2008 by The McGraw-Hill Companies, Inc. All rights reserved.

2 3 4 5 6 7 8 9 0 BKM/BKM 0 9 8 7

ISBN: 978-0-07-328346-3
MHID: 0-07-328346-0

www.mhhe.com

# Contents

**Solutions to the Exercises**

# Preface

This manual includes solutions to odd and selected even exercises in *Elementary Statistics: A Brief Version,* Fourth Edition, by Allan G. Bluman. Solutions are worked out step-by-step where appropriate and generally follow the same procedures used in the examples in the textbook. Answers may be carried to several decimal places to increase accuracy and to facilitate checking. See your instructor for specific rounding rules. Graphs are included with the solutions when appropriate or required. They are intended to convey a general idea and may not be to scale.

Caution: Answers generated using graphing calculators such as the TI-83 may vary from those shown in this manual.

To maximize the assistance provided in this manual, you should:

1. Read each section of the text carefully, noting examples and formulas.

2. Begin working the exercises using textbook examples and class notes as your guide, then refer to the answers in this manual.

3. Many instructors require students to interpret their answers within the context of the problem. These interpretations are powerful tools to understanding the meaning and purpose of each calculation. You should attempt to interpret each calculation even if you are not required to do so.

4. Be sure to show your work. When checking your work for errors you will need to review each step. When preparing for exams, reviewing each step helps you to recall the process involved in producing each calculation.

5. As you gain confidence and understanding, you should attempt to work exercises without referring to examples or notes. Check each answer in the solutions manual before beginning the next exercise.

6. Slight variations between your answers and the answers in this manual are probably due to rounding differences and should not be a cause for concern. If you are concerned about these variations, check each step of your calculation again.

7. Many errors can be traced to the improper application of the rules for order of operations. You should first attempt to determine where and how your error occurred because diagnosing your error increases understanding and prevents future errors. See your instructor if you are unsure of the location or cause of your error.

Sally H. Robinson

# Chapter 1 - The Nature of Probability and Statistics

REVIEW EXERCISES - CHAPTER 1

1. Descriptive statistics describes a set of data. Inferential statistics uses a set of data to make predictions about a population.

3. Answers will vary.

5. When the population is large, the researcher saves time and money using samples. Samples are used when the units must be destroyed.

6.
   a. Inferential     e. Inferential
   b. Descriptive     f. Inferential
   c. Descriptive     g. Descriptive
   d. Descriptive     h. Inferential

7.
   a. Ratio       f. Ordinal
   b. Ordinal     g. Ratio
   c. Ratio       h. Ratio
   d. Interval    i. Nominal
   e. Ratio       j. Ratio

8.
   a. Quantitative    e. Qualitative
   b. Qualitative     f. Quantitative
   c. Quantitative    g. Qualitative
   d. Quantitative

9.
   a. Discrete     e. Discrete
   b. Continuous   f. Discrete
   c. Continuous   g. Continuous
   d. Continuous

11. Random samples are selected by using chance methods or random numbers. Systematic samples are selected by numbering each subject and selecting every $k$th number. Stratified samples are selected by dividing the population into groups and selecting from each group. Cluster samples are selected by using intact groups called clusters.

12.
   a. Cluster       d. Systematic
   b. Systematic    e. Stratified
   c. Random

13. Answers will vary.

15. Answers will vary.

17.
   a. Experimental    c. Observational
   b. Observational   d. Experimental

19. Answers will vary. Possible answers include:
(a) overall health of participants, amount of exposure to infected individuals through the workplace or home
(b) gender and/or age of driver, time of day
(c) diet, general health, heredity factors
(d) amount of exercise, heredity factors

21. Claims can be proven only if the entire population is used.

23. Since the results are not typical, the advertisers selected only a few people for whom the product worked extremely well.

25. "74% more calories" than what? No comparison group is stated.

27. What is meant by "24 hours of acid control"?

29. Possible reasons for conflicting results: The amount of caffeine in the coffee or tea or the brewing method.

31. Answers will vary.

CHAPTER QUIZ
   1. True
   2. False, it is a data value.
   3. False, the highest level is ratio.
   4. False, it is stratified sampling.
   5. False, it is a quantitative variable.
   6. True
   7. False, it is 5.5-6.5 inches.
   8. c
   9. b
   10. d
   11. a
   12. c
   13. a
   14. Descriptive, inferential
   15. Gambling, insurance
   16. Population
   17. Sample

18.
a. Saves time
b. Saves money
c. Use when population is infinite

19.
  a. Random     c. Cluster
  b. Systematic  d. Stratified

20. Quasi-experimental

21. Random

22.
  a. Descriptive  d. Inferential
  b. Inferential    e. Inferential
  c. Descriptive

23.
  a. Nominal   d. Interval
  b. Ratio     e. Ratio
  c. Ordinal

24.
  a. Continuous  d. Continuous
  b. Discrete    e. Discrete
  c. Continuous

25.
  a. $47.5 - 48.5$ seconds    d. $13.65 - 13.75$ pounds
  b. $0.555 - 0.565$ centimeters  e. $6.5 - 7.5$ feet
  c. $9.05 - 9.15$ quarts

# Chapter 2 - Frequency Distributions and Graphs

## EXERCISE SET 2-2

1. Frequency distributions are used to organize data in a meaningful way, to facilitate computational procedures for statistics, to make it easier to draw charts and graphs, and to make comparisons among different sets of data.

3.
a. $11.5 - 18.5$, $\frac{12+18}{2} = \frac{30}{2} = 15$, $18.5 - 11.5 = 7$
b. $55.5 - 74.5$, $\frac{56+74}{2} = \frac{130}{2} = 65$, $74.5 - 55.5 = 19$
c. $694.5 - 705.5$, $\frac{695+705}{2} = \frac{1400}{2} = 700$, $705.5 - 694.5 = 11$
d. $13.55 - 14.75$, $\frac{13.6+14.7}{2} = \frac{28.3}{2} = 14.15$, $14.75 - 13.55 = 1.2$
e. $2.145 - 3.935$, $\frac{2.15+3.93}{2} = \frac{6.08}{2} = 3.04$, $3.935 - 2.145 = 1.79$

5.
a. Class width is not uniform.
b. Class limits overlap, and class width is not uniform.
c. A class has been omitted.
d. Class width is not uniform.

7.

| Class | Tally | f | Percent |
|---|---|---|---|
| A | IIII | 4 | 10% |
| M | III III III III III III | 28 | 70% |
| H | III I | 6 | 15% |
| S | II | 2 | 5% |
| | | 40 | 100% |

9.

| Limits | Boundaries | f | cf |
|---|---|---|---|
| 19 - 21 | 18.5 - 21.5 | 2 | 2 |
| 22 - 24 | 21.5 - 24.5 | 13 | 15 |
| 25 - 27 | 24.5 - 27.5 | 11 | 26 |
| 28 - 30 | 27.5 - 30.5 | 3 | 29 |
| 31 - 33 | 30.5 - 33.5 | 1 | 30 |
| | | 30 | |

The average speed is about 24.5 mph.

11. H = 780   L = 746
Range = 780 − 746 = 34
Width = 34 ÷ 6 = 5.$\overline{6}$ or 6; round up to 7

11. continued

| Limits | Boundaries | f | cf |
|---|---|---|---|
| 745 - 751 | 744.5 - 751.5 | 4 | 4 |
| 752 - 758 | 751.5 - 758.5 | 5 | 9 |
| 759 - 765 | 758.5 - 765.5 | 7 | 16 |
| 766 - 772 | 765.5 - 772.5 | 11 | 27 |
| 773 - 779 | 772.5 - 779.5 | 2 | 29 |
| 780 - 786 | 779.5 - 786.5 | 1 | 30 |
| | | 30 | |

13. H = 70   L = 27
Range = 70 − 27 = 43
Width = 43 ÷ 7 = 6.1 or 7

| Limits | Boundaries | f | cf |
|---|---|---|---|
| 27 - 33 | 26.5 - 33.5 | 7 | 7 |
| 34 - 40 | 33.5 - 40.5 | 14 | 21 |
| 41 - 47 | 40.5 - 47.5 | 15 | 36 |
| 48 - 54 | 47.5 - 54.5 | 11 | 47 |
| 55 - 61 | 54.5 - 61.5 | 3 | 50 |
| 62 - 68 | 61.5 - 68.5 | 3 | 53 |
| 69 - 75 | 68.5 - 75.5 | 2 | 55 |
| | | 55 | |

15.

| Limits | Boundaries | f | cf |
|---|---|---|---|
| 31 - 39 | 30.5 - 39.5 | 4 | 4 |
| 40 - 48 | 39.5 - 48.5 | 5 | 9 |
| 49 - 57 | 48.5 - 57.5 | 5 | 14 |
| 58 - 66 | 57.5 - 66.5 | 12 | 26 |
| 67 - 75 | 66.5 - 75.5 | 13 | 39 |
| 76 - 84 | 75.5 - 84.5 | 5 | 44 |
| 85 - 93 | 84.5 - 93.5 | 3 | 47 |
| | | 47 | |

17. H = 11,413   L = 150
Range = 11,413 − 150 = 11,263
Width = 11,263 ÷ 10 = 1126.3 or 1127

| Limits | Boundaries | f | cf |
|---|---|---|---|
| 150 - 1,276 | 149.5 - 1,276.5 | 2 | 2 |
| 1,277 - 2,403 | 1,276.5 - 2,403.5 | 2 | 4 |
| 2,404 - 3,530 | 2,403.5 - 3,530.5 | 5 | 9 |
| 3,531 - 4,657 | 3,530.5 - 4,657.5 | 8 | 17 |
| 4,658 - 5,784 | 4,657.5 - 5,784.5 | 7 | 24 |
| 5,785 - 6,911 | 5,784.5 - 6,911.5 | 3 | 27 |
| 6,912 - 8,038 | 6,911.5 - 8,038.5 | 7 | 34 |
| 8,039 - 9,165 | 8,038.5 - 9,165.5 | 3 | 37 |
| 9,166 - 10,292 | 9,165.5 - 10,292.5 | 3 | 40 |
| 10,293 - 11,419 | 10,292.5 - 11,419.5 | 2 | 42 |
| | | 42 | |

19. The percents add up to 101%. They should total 100% unless rounding was used.

EXERCISE SET 2-3

1.

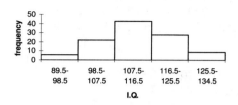

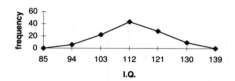

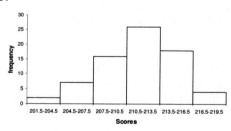

Eighty applicants do not need to enroll in the summer programs.

3.

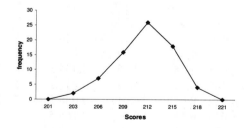

3. continued

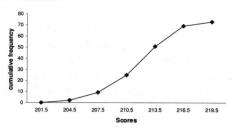

The distribution appears to be slightly left skewed.

5.

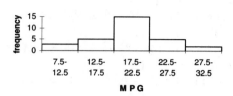

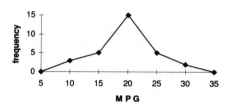

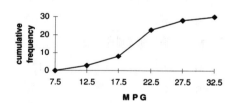

7.

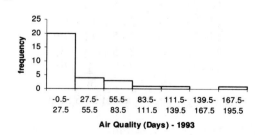

7. continued

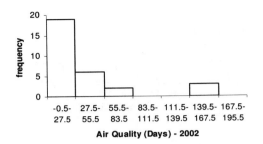

Both graphs are similar in that they are positively skewed. Also, it looks as if the air quality has improved somewhat in that there are slightly more smaller values in 2002, which means fewer days with unacceptable levels of pollution.

9.

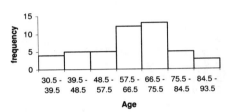

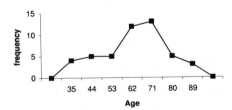

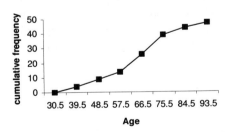

The histogram has a peak at the class of 66.5 – 75.5 and is somewhat negatively skewed.

11.

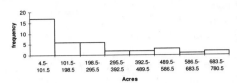

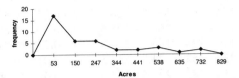

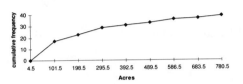

The peak is in the first class, and then the histogram is rather uniform after the first class. Most of the parks have less than 101.5 thousand acres as compared with any other class of values.

13.

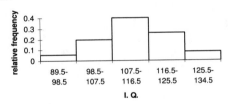

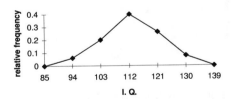

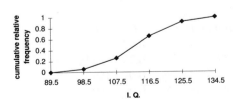

The proportion of applicants who need to enroll in a summer program is 0.26 or 26%.

15. H = 270   L = 80
Range = 270 − 80 = 190
Width = 190 ÷ 7 = 27.1 or 28
Use width = 29 (rule 2)

| Limits | Boundaries | f | rf | crf |
|--------|-----------|---|-----|------|
| 80 - 108 | 79.5 - 108.5 | 8 | 0.17 | 0.17 |
| 109 - 137 | 108.5 - 137.5 | 13 | 0.28 | 0.45 |
| 138 - 166 | 137.5 - 166.5 | 2 | 0.04 | 0.49 |
| 167 - 195 | 166.5 - 195.5 | 9 | 0.20 | 0.69 |
| 196 - 224 | 195.5 - 224.5 | 10 | 0.22 | 0.91 |
| 225 - 253 | 224.5 - 253.5 | 2 | 0.04 | 0.95 |
| 254 - 282 | 253.5 - 282.5 | 2 | 0.04 | 0.99* |
| | | | 0.99 | |

*due to rounding

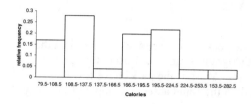

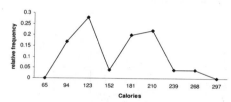

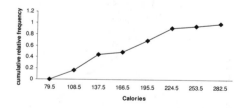

The histogram has two peaks.

17.

| Boundaries | rf | crf |
|-----------|------|------|
| -0.5 - 27.5 | 0.63 | 0.63 |
| 27.5 - 55.5 | 0.20 | 0.83 |
| 55.5 - 83.5 | 0.07 | 0.90 |
| 83.5 - 111.5 | 0.00 | 0.90 |
| 111.5 - 139.5 | 0.00 | 0.90 |
| 139.5 - 167.5 | 0.10 | 1.00 |
| 167.5 - 195.5 | 0.00 | 1.00 |
| | 100.0 | |

17. continued

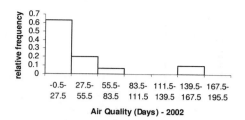

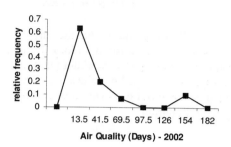

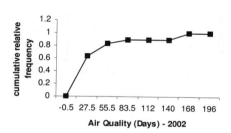

19.

a.

| Limits | Boundaries | $X_m$ | f | cf |
|--------|-----------|-------|---|-----|
| 22 - 24 | 21.5 - 24.5 | 23 | 1 | 1 |
| 25 - 27 | 24.5 - 27.5 | 26 | 3 | 4 |
| 28 - 30 | 27.5 - 30.5 | 29 | 0 | 4 |
| 31 - 33 | 30.5 - 33.5 | 32 | 6 | 10 |
| 34 - 36 | 33.5 - 36.5 | 35 | 5 | 15 |
| 37 - 39 | 36.5 - 39.5 | 38 | 3 | 18 |
| 40 - 42 | 39.5 - 42.5 | 41 | 2 | 20 |
| | | | 20 | |

b.

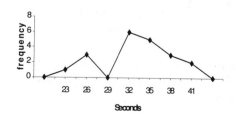

6

19. continued
c.

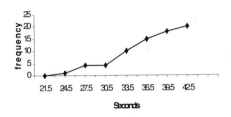

EXERCISE SET 2-4

1.

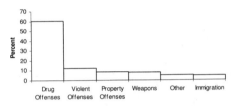

The majority of the money should be spent for drug rehabilitation.

3.

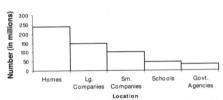

The best place to market products would be to residential users.

5.

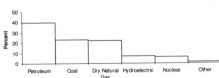

7.

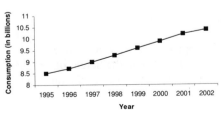

7. continued
There is a steady increase in consumption of tobacco products.

9.

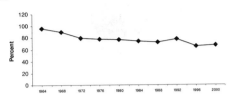

The graph shows a decline in the percentages of registered voters voting in presidential elections.

11.

| Principal Residence | 7.8% | 28.08° |
|---|---|---|
| Liquid Assets | 5.0% | 18.0° |
| Pension Accounts | 6.9% | 24.84° |
| Stocks, Funds, and Trusts | 31.6% | 113.76° |
| Business & Real Estate | 46.9% | 168.84° |
| Miscellaneous | 1.8% | 6.48° |
| | 100.0% | 360.00° |

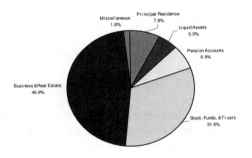

13.

| Career change | 34% | 122.4° |
|---|---|---|
| New job | 29% | 104.4° |
| Start business | 21% | 75.6° |
| Retire | 16% | 57.6° |
| | 100% | 360.0° |

13. continued
Pie chart:

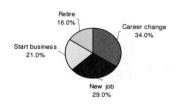

Pareto chart:

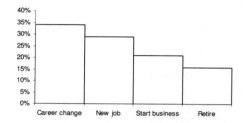

The pie graph better represents the data
since we are looking at parts of a whole.

15.

```
4 | 2  3
4 | 6  6  7  8  9  9
5 | 0  1  1  1  1  2  2  4  4  4  4  4
5 | 5  5  5  5  6  6  6  7  7  7  7  8
6 | 0  1  1  1  2  4  4
6 | 5  8  9
```

The distribution is somewhat symmetric and
unimodal. The majority of the Presidents
were in their 50's when inaugurated.

17.

```
        Variety 1                    Variety 2
                    2 | 1 | 3  8
                  3 0 | 2 | 5
            9 8 8 5 2 | 3 | 6  8
              3 3 1 | 4 | 1  2  5  5
  9 9 8 5 3 3 2 1 0 | 5 | 0  3  5  5  6  7  9
                    | 6 | 2  2
```

The distributions are similar but variety 2
seems to be more variable than variety 1.

19.

```
1 | 3  4  8  9
2 | 5  8  9
3 | 2  8
4 | 1
```

21.

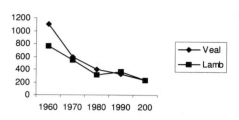

In 1960, veal production was considerably
higher than lamb. By 1970, production was
approximately the same for both.

23.

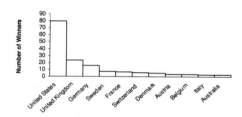

25. The values on the $y$ axis start at 3.5.
Also there are no data values shown for the
years 2004 through 2011.

EXERCISE SET 2-5

1. scatter plot or scatter diagram

3. Two variables are positively related when
the dependent variable, $y$, increases as the
independent variable, $x$, increases. The
points on the scatter plot fall approximately
in an ascending straight line.

5.

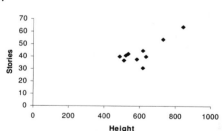

There appears to be a positive linear
relationship between the height of a building
and the number of stories in the building.

7.

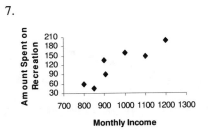

There appears to be a positive linear relationship between monthly income and amount spent on recreation.

9.

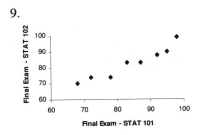

There appears to be a positive linear realationship between a student's final exam score in STAT 101 and STAT 102.

11.

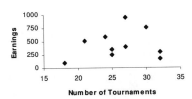

There appears to be neither a positive nor negative linear relationship between the number of tournaments and the earnings of LPGA golfers.

13.

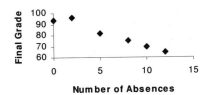

There appears to be a negative linear relationship between the number of absences and at student's final grade in a course.

REVIEW EXERCISES - CHAPTER 2

1.

| Class | f |
|---|---|
| Newspaper | 10 |
| Television | 16 |
| Radio | 12 |
| Internet | 12 |
| | 50 |

3.

| Class | f |
|---|---|
| baseball | 4 |
| golf ball | 5 |
| tennis ball | 6 |
| soccer ball | 5 |
| football | 5 |
| | 25 |

5.

| Class | f | cf |
|---|---|---|
| 11 | 1 | 1 |
| 12 | 2 | 3 |
| 13 | 2 | 5 |
| 14 | 2 | 7 |
| 15 | 1 | 8 |
| 16 | 2 | 10 |
| 17 | 4 | 14 |
| 18 | 2 | 16 |
| 19 | 2 | 18 |
| 20 | 1 | 19 |
| 21 | 0 | 19 |
| 22 | 1 | 20 |
| | 20 | |

7.

| Limits | Boundaries | f | cf |
|---|---|---|---|
| 85 - 105 | 84.5 - 105.5 | 4 | 4 |
| 106 - 126 | 105.5 - 126.5 | 7 | 11 |
| 127 - 147 | 126.5 - 147.5 | 9 | 20 |
| 148 - 168 | 147.5 - 168.5 | 10 | 30 |
| 169 - 189 | 168.5 - 189.5 | 9 | 39 |
| 190 - 210 | 189.5 - 210.5 | 1 | 40 |
| | | 40 | |

9.

| Limits | Boundaries | f | cf |
|---|---|---|---|
| 170 - 188 | 169.5 - 188.5 | 11 | 11 |
| 189 - 207 | 188.5 - 207.5 | 9 | 20 |
| 208 - 226 | 207.5 - 226.5 | 4 | 24 |
| 227 - 245 | 226.5 - 245.5 | 5 | 29 |
| 246 - 264 | 245.5 - 264.5 | 0 | 29 |
| 265 - 283 | 264.5 - 283.5 | 0 | 29 |
| 284 - 302 | 283.5 - 302.5 | 0 | 29 |
| 303 - 321 | 302.5 - 321.5 | 1 | 30 |
| | | 30 | |

11.

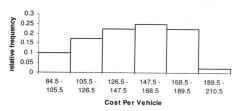

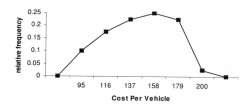

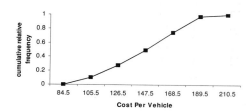

13.

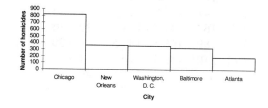

15.

The minimum wage has increased over the years with the largest increase occurring between 1975 and 1980.

17.

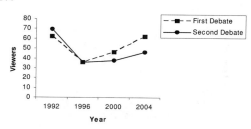

About the same number of people watched the first and second debates in 1992 and 1996. After that more people watched the first debate than watched the second debate.

19.

The majority of people surveyed would like to spend the rest of their careers with their present employer.

21.

```
1 | 2  4
1 | 6  7  8  8  9
2 | 0  2  3  4
2 | 5  5  5  6  6  9  9
3 | 2  3
3 | 5  7  8  8  9
```

The peak of the distribution is in the range of 25 − 29.

23.

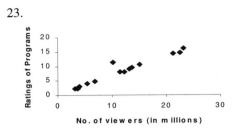

There appears to be a positive linear relationship between the number of viewers (in millions) and the ratings of 15 television programs.

CHAPTER 2 QUIZ

1. False
2. False
3. False
4. True
5. True
6. False
7. False
8. c
9. c
10. b
11. b
12. Categorical, ungrouped, grouped
13. 5, 20
14. Categorical
15. Time series
16. Stem and leaf plot
17. Vertical or y

18.

| Class | f | cf |
|---|---|---|
| H | 6 | 6 |
| A | 5 | 11 |
| M | 6 | 17 |
| C | 8 | 25 |
| | 25 | |

19.

20.

| Class | f | cf |
|---|---|---|
| 0.5 − 1.5 | 1 | 1 |
| 1.5 − 2.5 | 5 | 6 |
| 2.5 − 3.5 | 3 | 9 |
| 3.5 − 4.5 | 4 | 13 |
| 4.5 − 5.5 | 2 | 15 |
| 5.5 − 6.5 | 6 | 21 |
| 6.5 − 7.5 | 2 | 23 |
| 7.5 − 8.5 | 3 | 26 |
| 8.5 − 9.5 | 4 | 30 |
| | 30 | |

21.

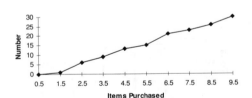

22.

| Limits | Boundaries | f | cf |
|---|---|---|---|
| 27 - 90 | 26.5 - 90.5 | 13 | 13 |
| 91 - 154 | 90.5 - 154.5 | 2 | 15 |
| 155 - 218 | 154.5 - 218.5 | 0 | 15 |
| 219 - 282 | 218.5 - 282.5 | 5 | 20 |
| 283 - 346 | 282.5 - 346.5 | 0 | 20 |
| 347 - 410 | 346.5 - 410.5 | 2 | 22 |
| 411 - 474 | 410.5 - 474.5 | 0 | 22 |
| 475 - 538 | 474.5 - 538.5 | 1 | 23 |
| 539 - 602 | 538.5 - 602.5 | 2 | 25 |
| | | 25 | |

23.
The distribution is positively skewed with one more than half of the data values in the lowest class.

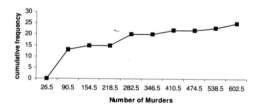

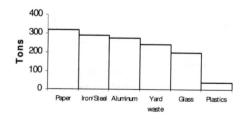

24.

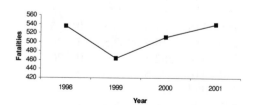

25.

Fatalities decreased in 1999 and then increased the next two years.

26.

```
1 | 5  9
2 | 6  8
3 | 1  5  8  8  9
4 | 1  7  8
5 | 3  3  4
6 | 2  3  7  8
7 | 6  9
8 | 6  8  9
9 | 8
```

27.

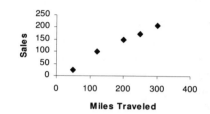

There appears to be a positive linear relationship between the number of miles traveled and the sales (in hundreds of dollars) of a sales representative.

Note: Answers may vary due to rounding, TI 83's, or computer programs.

EXERCISE SET 3-2

1.
$\overline{X} = \frac{\Sigma X}{n} = \frac{93.09}{25} = 3.7236 \approx 3.724$

MD: 3.57, 3.64, 3.64, 3.65, 3.66, 3.67, 3.67, 3.68, 3.7, 3.7, 3.7, 3.73, **3.73**, 3.74, 3.74, 3.74, 3.75, 3.76, 3.77, 3.78, 3.78, 3.8, 3.8, 3.83, 3.86

Mode: 3.70 and 3.74     MR: $\frac{3.57 + 3.86}{2} = 3.715$

3.
$\overline{X} = \frac{\Sigma X}{n} = \frac{136}{9} = 15.1$

MD: 1, 2, 3, 3, **7**, 11, 18, 30, 61

Mode = 3     MR $= \frac{1+61}{2} = 31$

For the best measure of average, answers will vary.

5.
$\overline{X} = \frac{\Sigma X}{n} = \frac{3249}{12} = 270.75$ or 270.8

MD: 75, 88, 102, 117, 136, **189, 229,** 239, 372, 465, 574, 663 MD $= \frac{189+229}{2} = 209$

Mode: no mode     MR $= \frac{75+663}{2} = 369$

It would seem that the average number of identity thefts is not higher than 300.

7.
$\overline{X} = \frac{\Sigma X}{n} = \frac{79.6}{12} = 6.63$

MD: 5.4, 5.4, 6.2, 6.2, 6.4, **6.4, 6.5**, 7.0, 7.2, 7.2, 7.7, 8.0          MD $= \frac{6.4+6.5}{2} = 6.45$

Mode: no mode     MR $= \frac{5.4+8.0}{2} = 6.7$

For the best measure of average, answers will vary.

9.
$\overline{X} = \frac{\Sigma X}{n} = \frac{238,512}{42} = 5678.9$

MD: 150, 885, ..., **5315, 5370,** ..., 11070, 11413          MD $= \frac{5315+5370}{2} = 5342.5$

Mode: 4450     MR $= \frac{150+11,413}{2} = 5781.5$

The distribution is skewed to the right.

11.
For Year 1:

$\overline{X} = \frac{\Sigma X}{n} = \frac{24,911}{27} = 922.6$ MD $= 527$

11.  continued

Mode:  no mode          $MR = \frac{69+4192}{2} = 2130.5$

For Year 2:

$\overline{X} = \frac{\Sigma X}{n} = \frac{24,615}{2} = 911.7 \, MD = 485$

Mode:  1430          $MR = \frac{70+4040}{2} = 2055$

The mean, median, and midrange of the traffic fatalities for Year 2 are somewhat less than those for the Year 1 fatalities, indicating that the number of fatalities has decreased.

13.

| Class Limits | Boundaries | $X_m$ | f | $f \cdot X_m$ |
|---|---|---|---|---|
| 202 - 204 | 201.5 - 204.5 | 203 | 2 | 406 |
| 205 - 207 | 204.5 - 207.5 | 206 | 7 | 1442 |
| 208 - 210 | 207.5 - 210.5 | 209 | 16 | 3344 |
| 211 - 213 | 210.5 - 213.5 | 212 | 26 | 5512 |
| 214 - 216 | 213.5 - 216.5 | 215 | 18 | 3870 |
| 217 - 219 | 216.5 - 219.5 | 218 | 4 | 872 |
|  |  |  | 73 | 15,446 |

a.  $\overline{X} = \frac{\Sigma f \cdot X_m}{n} = \frac{15,446}{73} = 211.6$

b.  modal class:  $211 - 213$

15.

| Limits | Boundaries | $X_m$ | f | $f \cdot X_m$ |
|---|---|---|---|---|
| 34 - 96 | 33.5 - 96.5 | 65 | 13 | 845 |
| 97 - 159 | 96.5 - 159.5 | 128 | 2 | 256 |
| 160 - 222 | 159.5 - 222.5 | 191 | 0 | 0 |
| 223 - 285 | 222.5 - 285.5 | 254 | 5 | 1270 |
| 286 - 348 | 285.5 - 348.5 | 317 | 1 | 317 |
| 349 - 411 | 348.5 - 411.5 | 380 | 1 | 380 |
| 412 - 474 | 411.5 - 474.5 | 443 | 0 | 0 |
| 475 - 537 | 474.5 - 537.5 | 506 | 1 | 506 |
| 538 - 600 | 537.5 - 600.5 | 569 | 2 | 1138 |
|  |  |  | 25 | 4712 |

a.  $\overline{X} = \frac{\Sigma f \cdot X_m}{n} = \frac{4712}{25} = 188.48$

b.  modal class:  $34 - 96$

Since most of the data is in the lowest class, the mean is probably not the best measure of average.  If the individual data values are available, the median may be a better measure of average.  A procedure for finding the approximate median for grouped data is found in Exercise 42 of this section.

17.

| Boundaries | $X_m$ | $f$ | $f \cdot X_m$ |
|---|---|---|---|
| 52.5 – 63.5 | 58 | 6 | 348 |
| 63.5 – 74.5 | 69 | 12 | 828 |
| 74.5 – 85.5 | 80 | 25 | 2000 |
| 85.5 – 96.5 | 91 | 18 | 1638 |
| 96.5 – 107.5 | 102 | 14 | 1428 |
| 107.5 – 118.5 | 113 | 5 | 565 |
| | | 80 | 6807 |

a. $\overline{X} = \dfrac{\sum f \cdot X_m}{n} = \dfrac{6807}{80} = 85.1$

b. modal class: $74.5 - 85.5$

19.

| Class Limits | Boundaries | $X_m$ | $f$ | $f \cdot X_m$ |
|---|---|---|---|---|
| 13 – 19 | 12.5 – 19.5 | 16 | 2 | 32 |
| 20 – 26 | 19.5 – 26.5 | 23 | 7 | 161 |
| 27 – 33 | 26.5 – 33.5 | 30 | 12 | 360 |
| 34 – 40 | 33.5 – 40.5 | 37 | 5 | 185 |
| 41 – 47 | 40.5 – 47.5 | 44 | 6 | 264 |
| 48 – 54 | 47.5 – 54.5 | 51 | 1 | 51 |
| 55 – 61 | 54.5 – 61.5 | 58 | 0 | 0 |
| 62 – 68 | 61.5 – 68.5 | 65 | 2 | 130 |
| | | | 35 | 1183 |

a. $\overline{X} = \dfrac{\sum f \cdot X_m}{n} = \dfrac{1183}{35} = 33.8$

b. modal class: $27 - 33$

21.

| Boundaries | $X_m$ | $f$ | $f \cdot X_m$ |
|---|---|---|---|
| 15.5 – 18.5 | 17 | 14 | 238 |
| 18.5 – 21.5 | 20 | 12 | 240 |
| 21.5 – 24.5 | 23 | 18 | 414 |
| 24.5 – 27.5 | 26 | 10 | 260 |
| 27.5 – 30.5 | 29 | 15 | 435 |
| 30.5 – 33.5 | 32 | 6 | 192 |
| | | 75 | 1779 |

a. $\overline{X} = \dfrac{\sum f \cdot X_m}{n} = \dfrac{1779}{75} = 23.7$

b. modal class: $21.5 - 24.5$

23.

| Limits | Boundaries | $X_m$ | $f$ | $f \cdot X_m$ |
|---|---|---|---|---|
| 27 - 33 | 26.5 - 33.5 | 30 | 7 | 210 |
| 34 - 40 | 33.5 - 40.5 | 37 | 14 | 518 |
| 41 - 47 | 40.5 - 47.5 | 44 | 15 | 660 |
| 48 - 54 | 47.5 - 54.5 | 51 | 11 | 561 |
| 55 - 61 | 54.5 - 61.5 | 58 | 3 | 174 |
| 62 - 68 | 61.5 - 68.5 | 65 | 3 | 195 |
| 69 - 75 | 68.5 - 75.5 | 72 | 2 | 144 |
| | | | 55 | 2462 |

$$\overline{X} = \frac{\sum f \cdot X_m}{n} = \frac{2462}{55} = 44.8$$

modal class: $40.5 - 47.5$

25.

| Limits | Boundaries | $X_m$ | $f$ | $f \cdot X_m$ |
|---|---|---|---|---|
| 31 - 39 | 30.5 - 39.5 | 35 | 4 | 140 |
| 40 - 48 | 39.5 - 48.5 | 44 | 5 | 220 |
| 49 - 57 | 48.5 - 57.5 | 53 | 5 | 265 |
| 58 - 66 | 57.5 - 66.5 | 62 | 12 | 744 |
| 67 - 75 | 66.5 - 75.5 | 71 | 13 | 923 |
| 76 - 84 | 75.5 - 84.5 | 80 | 5 | 400 |
| 85 - 93 | 84.5 - 93.5 | 89 | 3 | 267 |
| | | | 47 | 2959 |

$$\overline{X} = \frac{\sum f \cdot X_m}{n} = \frac{2959}{47} = 62.96 \text{ or } 63.0$$

modal class: $66.5 - 75.5$

27.

$$\overline{X} = \frac{\sum w \cdot X}{\sum w} = \frac{3(3.33) + 3(3.00) + 2(2.5) + 2.5(4.4) + 4(1.75)}{3 + 3 + 2 + 2.5 + 4} = \frac{41.99}{14.5} = 2.896$$

29.

$$\overline{X} = \frac{\sum w \cdot X}{\sum w} = \frac{9(427000) + 6(365000) + 12(725000)}{9 + 6 + 12} = \frac{14,733,000}{27} = \$545,666.67$$

31.

$$\overline{X} = \frac{\sum w \cdot X}{\sum w} = \frac{1(62) + 1(83) + 1(97) + 1(90) + 2(82)}{6} = \frac{496}{6} = 82.7$$

33.
a. Median
b. Mean
c. Mode
d. Mode
e. Mode
f. Mean

35.
Both could be true since one could be using the mean for the average salary, and the other could be using the mode for the average.

37.
$5 \cdot 8.2 = 41$
$6 + 10 + 7 + 12 + x = 41$
$x = 6$

39.
a. $\dfrac{2}{\frac{1}{30} + \frac{1}{45}} = 36$ mph

b. $\dfrac{2}{\frac{1}{40} + \frac{1}{25}} = 30.77$ mph

c. $\dfrac{2}{\frac{1}{50} + \frac{1}{10}} = \$16.67$

41.

$$\sqrt{\frac{8^2 + 6^2 + 3^2 + 5^2 + 4^2}{5}} = \sqrt{30} = 5.48$$

EXERCISE SET 3-3

1.
The square root of the variance is equal to the standard deviation.

3.
$\sigma^2, \sigma$

5.
When the sample size is less than 30, the formula for the true standard deviation of the sample will underestimate the population standard deviation.

7.
R = 48 − 0 = 48

$$s^2 = \frac{\sum X^2 - \frac{(\sum X)^2}{n}}{n-1} = \frac{4061 - \frac{(133)^2}{10}}{10-1} = \frac{2292.1}{9} = 254.68 \approx 254.7$$

$s = \sqrt{254.7} = 15.96 \approx 16$    The data vary widely.

9.
For Temperature:
R = 61 − 29 = 32

$$s^2 = \frac{\sum X^2 - \frac{(\sum X)^2}{n}}{n-1} = \frac{20{,}777 - \frac{441^2}{10}}{10-1} = 147.66$$

$s = \sqrt{147.66} = 12.15$

For Precipitation:
R = 5.1 − 1.1 = 4.0

$$s^2 = \frac{\sum X^2 - \frac{(\sum X)^2}{n}}{n-1} = \frac{86.13 - \frac{26.3^2}{10}}{10-1} = 1.88$$

$s = \sqrt{1.88} = 1.37$

Temperature is more variable.

11.
St. Paul, MN:
$R = 46 - 16 = 30$

$$s^2 = \frac{\sum X^2 - \frac{(\sum X)^2}{n}}{n-1} = \frac{9677 - \frac{313^2}{11}}{11-1} = \frac{770.727}{10} = 77.1$$

$$s = \sqrt{77.1} = 8.8$$

Chicago, IL:
$R = 100 - 57 = 43$

$$s^2 = \frac{\sum X^2 - \frac{(\sum X)^2}{n}}{n-1} = \frac{59,980 - \frac{796^2}{11}}{11-1} = \frac{2378.545}{10} = 237.85 \approx 237.9$$

$$s = \sqrt{237.9} = 15.4$$

The data for Chicago is more variable since the standard deviation is much larger.

13.
$R = 22 - 1 = 21$

$$s^2 = \frac{\sum X^2 - \frac{(\sum X)^2}{n}}{n-1} = \frac{1061 - \frac{89^2}{15}}{15-1} = 38.1$$

$$s = \sqrt{38.1} = 6.2$$

Using the range rule of thumb, $s \approx \frac{22-1}{4} = 5.25$.  The estimate is close.

15.
For 1995:
$R = 4192 - 69 = 4123$

$$s^2 = \frac{\sum X^2 - \frac{(\sum X)^2}{n}}{n-1} = \frac{49,784,885 - \frac{24,911^2}{27}}{27-1} = 1,030,817.63$$

$$s = \sqrt{1,030,817.63} = 1015.3$$

For 1996:
$R = 4040 - 70 = 3970$

$$s^2 = \frac{\sum X^2 - \frac{(\sum X)^2}{n}}{n-1} = \frac{48,956,875 - \frac{24,615^2}{27}}{27-1} = 1,019,853.85$$

$$s = \sqrt{1,019,853.85} = 1009.9$$

The fatalities in 1995 are more variable.

17.
$R = 11,413 - 150 = 11,263$

$$s^2 = \frac{\sum X^2 - \frac{(\sum X)^2}{n}}{n-1} = \frac{1,659,371,050 - \frac{238,512^2}{42}}{42-1} = \frac{304,895,475.1}{41} = 7,436,475.003$$

$$s = \sqrt{7,436,475.003} = 2726.99 \text{ or } 2727$$

19.

| $X_m$ | f | $f \cdot X_m$ | $f \cdot X_m^2$ |
|---|---|---|---|
| 16 | 2 | 32 | 512 |
| 23 | 7 | 161 | 3703 |
| 30 | 12 | 360 | 10,800 |
| 37 | 5 | 185 | 6845 |
| 44 | 6 | 264 | 11,616 |
| 51 | 1 | 51 | 2601 |
| 58 | 0 | 0 | 0 |
| 65 | 2 | 130 | 8450 |
|  | 35 | 1183 | 44527 |

$$s^2 = \frac{\sum f \cdot X_m^2 - \frac{(\sum f \cdot X_m)^2}{n}}{n-1} = \frac{44,527 - \frac{1183^2}{35}}{35-1} = \frac{4541.6}{34} = 133.58 \text{ or } 133.6$$

$$s = \sqrt{133.58} = 11.6$$

21.

| $X_m$ | f | $f \cdot X_m$ | $f \cdot X_m^2$ |
|---|---|---|---|
| 65 | 13 | 845 | 54,925 |
| 128 | 2 | 256 | 32,768 |
| 191 | 0 | 0 | 0 |
| 254 | 5 | 1270 | 322,580 |
| 317 | 1 | 317 | 100,489 |
| 380 | 1 | 380 | 144,400 |
| 443 | 0 | 0 | 0 |
| 506 | 1 | 506 | 256,036 |
| 569 | 2 | 1138 | 647,522 |
|  |  | 4712 | 1,558,720 |

$$s^2 = \frac{\sum f \cdot X_m^2 - \frac{(\sum f \cdot X_m)^2}{n}}{n-1} = \frac{1,558,720 - \frac{4712^2}{25}}{25-1} = \frac{670,602.24}{24} = 27,941.76$$

$$s = \sqrt{27941.76} = 167.16 \text{ or } 167.2$$

23.

| $X_m$ | f | $f \cdot X_m$ | $f \cdot X_m^2$ |
|---|---|---|---|
| 58 | 6 | 348 | 20,184 |
| 69 | 12 | 828 | 57,132 |
| 80 | 25 | 2000 | 160,000 |
| 91 | 18 | 1638 | 148,058 |
| 102 | 14 | 1428 | 145,656 |
| 112 | 5 | 565 | 63,845 |
|  | 80 | 6807 | 595,875 |

$$s^2 = \frac{\sum f \cdot X_m^2 - \frac{(\sum f \cdot X_m)^2}{n}}{n-1} = \frac{59,5875 - \frac{6807^2}{80}}{80-1} = \frac{16,684.39}{79} = 211.2$$

$$s = \sqrt{211.2} = 14.5$$

25.

| $X_m$ | f | $f \cdot X_m$ | $f \cdot X_m^2$ |
|---|---|---|---|
| 68 | 5 | 340 | 23,120 |
| 79 | 14 | 1106 | 87,374 |
| 90 | 18 | 1620 | 145,800 |
| 101 | 25 | 2525 | 255,025 |
| 112 | 12 | 1344 | 150,528 |
| 123 | 6 | 738 | 90,774 |
| | 80 | 7673 | 752,621 |

$$s^2 = \frac{\sum f \cdot X_m^2 - \frac{(\sum f \cdot X_m)^2}{n}}{n-1} = \frac{752,621 - \frac{7673^2}{80}}{80-1} = \frac{16,684.3875}{79} = 211.19 \text{ or } 211.2$$

$$s = \sqrt{211.2} = 14.5$$

No, the variability of the lifetimes of the batteries is quite large.

27.

| $X_m$ | f | $f \cdot X_m$ | $f \cdot X_m^2$ |
|---|---|---|---|
| 27 | 5 | 135 | 3645 |
| 30 | 9 | 270 | 8100 |
| 33 | 32 | 1056 | 34848 |
| 36 | 30 | 720 | 25920 |
| 39 | 12 | 468 | 18252 |
| 62 | 2 | 84 | 3528 |
| | 80 | 2733 | 94293 |

$$s^2 = \frac{\sum f \cdot X_m^2 - \frac{(\sum f \cdot X_m)^2}{n}}{n-1} = \frac{94,293 - \frac{2733^2}{80}}{80-1} = \frac{926.89}{79} = 11.7$$

$$s = \sqrt{11.7} = 3.4$$

29.
For East: $\overline{X} = 2660$, $s = 991.9$; C. Var $= \frac{s}{\overline{X}} = \frac{991.9}{2660} = 0.373$ or 37.3%

For West: $\overline{X} = 2261.2$, $s = 1117.9$; C. Var $= \frac{s}{\overline{X}} = \frac{1117.9}{2261.2} = 0.494$ or 49.4%
The data for the West is more variable.

31.
C. Var $= \frac{s}{\overline{X}} = \frac{6}{26} = 0.231 = 23.1\%$

C. Var $= \frac{s}{\overline{X}} = \frac{4000}{31,000} = 0.129 = 12.9\%$
The age is more variable.

33.

a. $1 - \frac{1}{5^2} = 0.96$ or 96%

b. $1 - \frac{1}{4^2} = 0.9375$ or 93.75%

**35.**
$\overline{X} = 5.02 \quad s = 0.09$
At least 75% of the data values will fall withing two standard deviations of the mean; hence,
$2(\$0.09) = \$0.18$ and $\$5.02 - \$0.18 = \$4.84$ and $\$5.02 + \$0.18 = \$5.20$. Hence at least 75% of the data values will fall between $4.84 and $5.20.

**37.**
$\overline{X} = 95 \quad s = 2$
At least 88.89% of the data values will fall within 3 standard deviations of the mean, hence
$95 - 3(2) = 89$ and $95 + 3(2) = 101$. Therefore at least 88.89% of the data values will fall between 89 mg and 101 mg.

**39.**
$\overline{X} = 12 \quad s = 3$
$20 - 12 = 8$ and $8 \div 3 = 2.67$
Hence, $1 - \frac{1}{k^2} = 1 - \frac{1}{2.67^2} = 1 - 0.14 = 0.86 = 86\%$
At least 86% of the data values will fall between 4 and 20.

**41.**
$26.8 + 1(4.2) = 31$
By the Empirical Rule, 68% of consumption is within 1 standard deviation of the mean. Then $\frac{1}{2}$ of 32%, or 16%, of consumption would be more than 31 pounds of citrus fruit per year.

**43.**
$n = 30 \quad \overline{X} = 214.97 \quad s = 20.76$ At least 75% of the data values will fall between $\overline{X} \pm 2s$.
$\overline{X} - 2(20.76) = 214.97 - 41.52 = 173.45$ and $\overline{X} + 2(20.76) = 214.97 + 41.52 = 256.49$
In this case all 30 values fall within this range; hence Chebyshev's Theorem is correct for this example.

**45.**
For k = 1.5, $1 - \frac{1}{1.5^2} = 1 - 0.44 = 0.56$ or 56%
For k = 2, $1 - \frac{1}{2^2} = 1 - 0.25 = 0.75$ or 75%
For k = 2.5, $1 - \frac{1}{2.5^2} = 1 - 0.16 = 0.84$ or 84%
For k = 3, $1 - \frac{1}{3^2} = 1 - 0.1111 = .8889$ or 88.89%
For k = 3.5, $1 - \frac{1}{3.5^2} = 1 - 0.08 = 0.92$ or 92%

**47.**
$\overline{X} = 13.3$
$\text{Mean Dev} = \frac{|5-13.3|+|9-13.3|+|10-13.3|+|11-13.3|+|11-13.3|}{10}$

$+ \frac{|12-13.3|+|15-13.3|+|18-13.3|+|20-13.3|+|22-13.3|}{10} = 4.36$

**49.**
For $n = 25$, $\overline{X} = 50$, and $s = 3$:

$s\sqrt{n-1} = 3\sqrt{25-1} = 14.7 \qquad \overline{X} + s\sqrt{n-1} = 50 + 14.7 = 64.7$

67 must be an incorrect data value, since is beyond the range using the formula $s\sqrt{n-1}$.

**EXERCISE SET 3-4**

**1.**
A z score tells how many standard deviations the data value is above or below the mean.

3.
A percentile is a relative measure while a percent is an absolute measure of the part to the total.

5.
$Q_1 = P_{25}, \; Q_2 = P_{50}, \; Q_3 = P_{75}$

7.
$D_1 = P_{10}, \; D_2 = P_{20}, \; D_3 = P_{30}$, etc

9.
a. $z = \dfrac{X - \overline{X}}{s} = \dfrac{136 - 127}{9} = 1$

b. $z = \dfrac{109 - 127}{9} = -2$

c. $z = \dfrac{104.5 - 127}{9} = -2.5$

d. $z = \dfrac{113.5 - 127}{9} = -1.5$

e. $z = \dfrac{133 - 127}{9} = 0.67$

11.
a. $z = \dfrac{X - \overline{X}}{s} = \dfrac{87 - 84}{4} = 0.75$

b. $z = \dfrac{79 - 84}{4} = -1.25$

c. $z = \dfrac{93 - 84}{4} = 2.25$

d. $z = \dfrac{76 - 84}{4} = -2$

e. $z = \dfrac{82 - 84}{4} = -0.5$

13.
a. $z = \dfrac{42 - 39}{4} = 0.75$

b. $z = \dfrac{76 - 71}{3} = 1.67$

The score for part b is has a higher relative position.

15.
a. $z = \dfrac{3.2 - 4.6}{1.5} = -0.93$    b. $z = \dfrac{630 - 800}{200} = -0.85$    c. $z = \dfrac{43 - 50}{5} = -1.4$

The score in part b is the highest.

17.
a. $21^{st}$    b. $58^{th}$    c. $77^{th}$    d. $33^{rd}$

18.
a. 7    b. 25    c. 64    d. 76    e. 93

19.
a. 235    b. 255    c. 261    d. 275    e. 283

20.
a. 376   b. 389   c. 432   d. 473   e. 498

21.
a. $17^{th}$   b. $39^{th}$   c. $53^{rd}$   d. $79^{th}$   e. $91^{st}$

23.
$c = \frac{6(30)}{100} = 1.8$ or 2        82

25.
$c = \frac{n \cdot p}{100} = \frac{7(60)}{100} = 4.2$ or 5    Hence, 47 is the closest value to the $60^{th}$ percentile.

27.
$c = \frac{10(40)}{100} = 4$        average the 4th and 5th values:  $P_{40} = \frac{2.1 + 2.2}{2} = 2.15$

29.
$c = \frac{6(33)}{100} = 1.98$ or 2        5, 12, 15, 16, 20, 21
                    $\uparrow P_{33}$

The second data value is 12.

31.
a.  5, 12, 16, 25, 32, 38      $Q_1 = 12, Q_2 = 20.5, Q_3 = 32$

Midquartile = $\frac{12 + 32}{2} = 22$      Interquartile range:  $32 - 12 = 20$

b. 53, 62, 78, 94, 96, 99, 103      $Q_1 = 62, Q_2 = 94, Q_3 = 99$

Midquartile = $\frac{62 + 99}{2} = 80.5$      Interquartile range:  $99 - 62 = 37$

EXERCISE SET 3-5

1. Data arranged in order:  6, 8, 12, 19, 27, 32, 54

Minimum:  6
$Q_1$:  8
Median:  19
$Q_3$:  32
Maximum:  54
Interquartile Range:  $32 - 8 = 24$

3. Data arranged in order:  188, 192, 316, 362, 437, 589

Minimum:  188
$Q_1$:  192
Median:  $\frac{316 + 362}{2} = 339$
$Q_3$:  437
Maximum:  589
Interquartile Range:  $437 - 192 = 245$

5. Data arranged in order: 14.6, 15.5, 16.3, 18.2, 19.8

Minimum: 14.6
$Q_1$: $\frac{14.6 + 15.5}{2} = 15.05$
Median: 16.3
$Q_3$: $\frac{18.2 + 19.8}{2} = 19.0$
Maximum: 19.8
Interquartile Range: $19.0 - 15.05 = 3.95$

7. Minimum: 3
$Q_1$: 5
Median: 8
$Q_3$: 9
Maximum: 11
Interquartile Range: $9 - 5 = 4$

9. Minimum: 55
$Q_1$: 65
Median: 70
$Q_3$: 90
Maximum: 95
Interquartile Range: $90 - 65 = 25$

11.
MD = $\frac{3.9 + 4.7}{2} = 4.3$
$Q_1 = 2.0$    $Q_3 = 7.6$

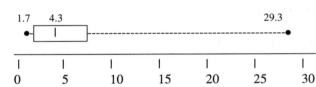

The distribution is positively skewed.

13. Data arranged in order: 13, 25, 25, 26, 28, 34, 35, 37, 42
Minimum: 13    Maximum: 42
MD = 28
$Q_1 = \frac{25 + 25}{2} = 25$ $Q_3 = \frac{35 + 37}{2} = 36$

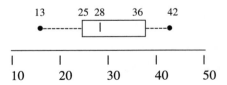

15. Data arranged in order: 3.2, 3.9, 4.4, 8.0, 9.8, 11.7, 13.9, 15.9, 17.6, 21.7, 24.8, 34.1
Minimum: 3.2    Maximum: 34.1

MD: $\frac{11.7 + 13.9}{2} = 12.8$

$Q_1$: $\frac{4.4 + 8.0}{2} = 6.2$          $Q_3$: $\frac{17.6 + 21.7}{2} = 19.65$

15. continued

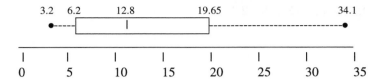

| 3.2 | 6.2 | 12.8 | 19.65 | 34.1 |

```
|     |     |     |     |     |     |     |     |
0     5     10    15    20    25    30    35
```

The distribution is positively skewed.

17.
(a)
For April: $\overline{X} = 149.3$
For May: $\overline{X} = 264.3$
For June: $\overline{X} = 224.0$
For July: $\overline{X} = 123.3$

The month with the highest mean number of tornadoes is May.

(b)
For 2001: $\overline{X} = 186.0$
For 2000: $\overline{X} = 165.0$
For 1999: $\overline{X} = 219.75$

The year with the highest mean number of tornadoes is 1999.

(c) The 5-number summaries for each year are:

For 2001:  120, 127.5, 188, 244.5, 248
For 2000:  135, 135.5, 142, 194.5, 241
For 1999:  102, 139.5, 233, 300, 311

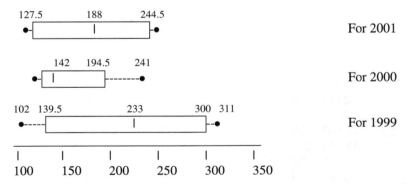

For 2001

For 2000

For 1999

The data for 2001 is approximately symmetric while the data for 2000 and 1999 are skewed. The data for 2000 is positively skewed and the data for 1999 is negatively skewed. The data for the year 2000 is the least variable and has the smallest median.

REVIEW EXERCISES - CHAPTER 3

1.
a. $\overline{X} = \dfrac{\sum X}{n} = \dfrac{1649}{15} = 109.9$

1. continued

b.    60, 68, 70, 75, 89, 93, 95, **97**, 112, 114, 114, 122, 128, 182, 229

MD $= 97$

c.  Mode $= 114$

d.  MR $= \frac{60+229}{2} = 144.5$

e.  Range $= 229 - 60 = 169$

f.  $s^2 = \dfrac{\sum X^2 - \frac{(\sum X)^2}{n}}{n-1} = \dfrac{209379 - \frac{1649^2}{15}}{15-1} = 2007.1$

g.  $s = \sqrt{2007.1} = 44.8$

3.

| Class | $X_m$ | f | $f \cdot X_m$ | $f \cdot X_m^2$ | cf |
|-------|-------|---|---------------|-----------------|-----|
| 1 - 3 | 2 | 1 | 2 | 4 | 1 |
| 4 - 6 | 5 | 4 | 20 | 100 | 5 |
| 7 - 9 | 8 | 5 | 40 | 320 | 10 |
| 10 - 12 | 11 | 1 | 11 | 121 | 11 |
| 13 - 15 | 14 | 1 | 14 | 196 | 12 |
|  |  | 12 | 87 | 741 |  |

a.  $\overline{X} = \dfrac{\sum f \cdot X_m}{n} = \frac{87}{12} = 7.3$

b.  Modal Class $= 7 - 9$ or $6.5 - 9.5$

c.  $s^2 = \dfrac{741 - \frac{87^2}{12}}{11} = \dfrac{110.25}{11} = 10.0$

f.  $s = \sqrt{10.0} = 3.2$

5.

| Class Boundaries | $X_m$ | f | $f \cdot X_m$ | $f \cdot X_m^2$ | cf |
|------------------|-------|---|---------------|-----------------|-----|
| 12.5 - 27.5 | 20 | 6 | 120 | 2400 | 6 |
| 27.5 - 42.5 | 35 | 3 | 105 | 3675 | 9 |
| 42.5 - 57.5 | 50 | 5 | 250 | 12,500 | 14 |
| 57.5 - 72.5 | 65 | 8 | 520 | 33,800 | 22 |
| 72.5 - 87.5 | 80 | 6 | 480 | 38,400 | 28 |
| 87.5 - 102.5 | 95 | 2 | 190 | 18,050 | 30 |
|  |  | 30 | 1665 | 108,825 |  |

a.  $\overline{X} = \dfrac{\sum f \cdot X_m}{n} = \frac{1665}{30} = 55.5$

b.  Modal class $= 57.5 - 72.5$

c.  $s^2 = \dfrac{\sum f \cdot X_m^2 - \frac{(\sum f \cdot X_m)^2}{n}}{n-1} = \dfrac{108825 - \frac{1665^2}{30}}{30-1} = \dfrac{16417.5}{29} = 566.1$

d.  $s = \sqrt{566.1} = 23.8$

7.
$$\overline{X} = \frac{\sum w \cdot X}{\sum w} = \frac{12 \cdot 0 + 8 \cdot 1 + 5 \cdot 2 + 5 \cdot 3}{12 + 8 + 5 + 5} = \frac{33}{30} = 1.1$$

9.
$$\overline{X} = \frac{\sum w \cdot X}{\sum w} = \frac{8 \cdot 3 + 1 \cdot 6 + 1 \cdot 30}{8 + 1 + 1} = \frac{60}{10} = 6$$

11.
Magazines: C. Var $= \frac{s}{\overline{X}} = \frac{12}{56} = 0.214$

Year: C. Var $= \frac{s}{\overline{X}} = \frac{2.5}{6} = 0.417$

The number of years is more variable.

13.
a.

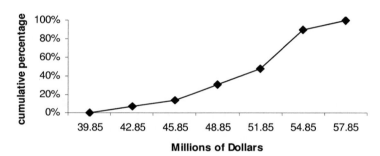

b. $P_{35} = 49$; $P_{65} = 52$; $P_{85} = 53$ (answers are approximate)
c. $44 = 15^{th}$ percentile; $48 = 33^{rd}$ percentile; $54 = 91^{nd}$ percentile
(answers are approximate)

15.
$\overline{X} = 0.32 \quad s = 0.03 \quad k = 2$
$0.32 - 2(0.03) = 0.26$ and $0.32 + 2(0.03) = 0.38$
At least 75% of the values will fall between \$0.26 and \$0.38.

17.
$\overline{X} = 54 \quad s = 4 \quad 60 - 54 = 6 \quad k = \frac{6}{4} = 1.5 \quad 1 - \frac{1}{1.5^2} = 1 - 0.44 = 0.56 \text{ or } 56\%$

19.
$\overline{X} = 32 \quad s = 4 \quad 44 - 32 = 12 \quad k = \frac{12}{4} = 3 \quad 1 - \frac{1}{3^2} = 0.8889 = 88.89\%$

21.
Before Christmas:
MD $= 30 \quad Q_1 = 21 \quad Q_3 = 33.5$

After Christmas:
MD $= 18 \quad Q_1 = 14.5 \quad Q_3 = 23$

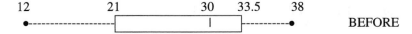

Chapter 3 - Data Description

21. continued

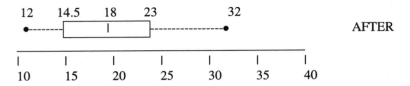

The employees worked more hours before Christmas than after Christmas. Also, the range and variability of the distribution of hours worked before Christmas is greater than that of hours worked after Christmas.

CHAPTER 3 QUIZ

1. True
2. True
3. False
4. False
5. False
6. False
7. False
8. False
9. False
10. c
11. c
12. a and b
13. b
14. d
15. b
16. Statistic
17. Parameters, statistics
18. Standard deviation
19. $\sigma$
20. Midrange
21. Positively
22. Outlier
23. a. 15.3   b. 15.5   c. 15, 16, 17   d. 15   e. 6   f. 3.61   g. 1.9
24. a. 6.4   b. $6-8$   c. 11.6   d. 3.4
25. a. 51.4   b. $35.5-50.5$   c. 451.5   d. 21.2
26. a. 8.2   b. $7-9$   c. 21.6   d. 4.6
27. 1.6
28. 4.46 or 4.5
29. 0.33; 0.162; newspapers
30. 0.3125; 0.229; brands
31. $-0.75$; $-1.67$; science
32. a. 0.5   b. 1.6   c. 15, c is higher
33. a. 56.25; 43.75; 81.25; 31.25; 93.75; 18.75; 6.25; 68.75   b. 0.9
    c.

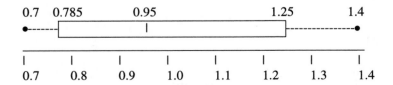

34.
a.

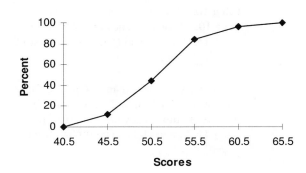

b. 47; 53; 65
c. $60^{th}$ percentile; $6^{th}$ percentile; $98^{th}$ percentile

35.
For Pre-buy:
MD = 1.62        $Q_1$ = 1.54        $Q_3$ = 1.65

For No Pre-buy:
MD = 3.95        $Q_1$ = 3.85        $Q_3$ = 3.99

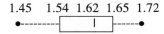

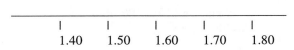

Pre-buy Cost

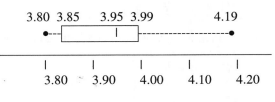

No Pre-buy Cost

The cost of pre-buy gas is much less than to return the car without filling it with gas. The variability of the return without filling with gas is larger than the variability of the pre-buy gas.

36.
For above 1129:  16%
For above 799:  97.5%

Note: Answers may vary due to rounding, TI-83's or computer programs.

EXERCISE SET 4-2

1.
A probability experiment is a chance process which leads to well-defined outcomes.

3.
An outcome is the result of a single trial of a probability experiment, whereas an event can consist of one or more outcomes.

5.
The range of values is $0 \leq P(E) \leq 1$.

7.
0

9.
$1 - 0.20 = 0.80$
Since the probability that it won't rain is 80%, you could leave your umbrella at home and be fairly safe.

11.
a. Empirical        e. Empirical
b. Classical        f. Empirical
c. Empirical        g. Subjective
d. Classical

12.
a. $\frac{1}{6}$     d. 1
b. $\frac{1}{2}$     e. 1
c. $\frac{1}{3}$     f. $\frac{5}{6}$
g. $\frac{1}{6}$

13.
There are $6^2$ or 36 outcomes.
a. There are 5 ways to get a sum of 6. They are (1,5), (2,4), (3,3), (4,2), and (5,1). The probability then is $\frac{5}{36}$.

b. There are six ways to get doubles. They are (1,1), (2,2), (3,3), (4,4), (5,5), and (6,6). The probability then is $\frac{6}{36} = \frac{1}{6}$.

c. There are six ways to get a sum of 7. They are (1,6), (2,5), (3,4), (4,3), (5,2), and (6,1). There are two ways to get a sum of 11. They are (5,6) and (6,5). Hence, the total number of ways to get a 7 or 11 is eight. The probability then is $\frac{8}{36} = \frac{2}{9}$.

13. continued
d. To get a sum greater than nine, one must roll a 10, 11, or 12. There are six ways to get a 10, 11, or 12. They are (4,6), (5,5), (6,4), (5,6), (6,5), and (6,6). The probability then is $\frac{6}{36} = \frac{1}{6}$.

e. To get a sum less than or equal to four, one must roll a 4, 3, or 2. There are six ways to do this. They are (3,1), (2,2), (1,3), (2,1), (1,2), and (1,1). The probability is $\frac{6}{36} = \frac{1}{6}$.

14.
a. $\frac{1}{13}$     f. $\frac{4}{13}$

b. $\frac{1}{4}$      g. $\frac{1}{2}$

c. $\frac{1}{52}$     h. $\frac{1}{26}$

d. $\frac{2}{13}$     i. $\frac{7}{13}$

e. $\frac{4}{13}$     j. $\frac{1}{26}$

15.
There are 24 possible outcomes.

a. P(winning $10) = P(rolling a 1)
P(rolling a 1) $= \frac{4}{24} = \frac{1}{6}$

b. P(winning $5 or $10) = P(rolling either a 1 or 2)
P(1 or 2) $= \frac{12}{24} = \frac{1}{2}$

c. P(winning a coupon) = P(rolling either a 3 or 4)
P(3 or 4) $= \frac{12}{24} = \frac{1}{2}$

17.
a. P(graduate school) $= \frac{110}{250} = \frac{11}{25}$ or 0.44

b. P(medical school) $= \frac{10}{250} = \frac{1}{25}$ or 0.04

c. P(not going to graduate school) $= 1 - \frac{110}{250} = \frac{140}{250}$ or 0.56

19.
a. P(2 or 3 children) $= 0.19 + 0.07 = 0.26$ or 26%

b. P(more than 1 child) $= 0.19 + 0.07 + 0.03 = 0.29$ or 29%

19. continued

c. P(less than 3 children) $= 0.51 + 0.20 + 0.19 = 0.90$ or 90%

d. The event in part c is most likely.

21.
The sample space is BBB, BBG, BGB, GBB, GGB, GBG, BGG, and GGG.

a. All boys is the outcome BBB; hence P(all boys) $= \frac{1}{8}$.

b. All girls or all boys would be BBB and GGG; hence, P(all girls or all boys) $= \frac{1}{4}$.

c. Exactly two boys or two girls would be BBG, BGB, GBB, BBG, GBG, or BGG. The probability then is $\frac{6}{8} = \frac{3}{4}$.

d. At least one child of each gender means at least one boy or at least one girl. The outcomes are the same as those of part c, hence the probability is the same, $\frac{3}{4}$.

23.
The outcomes for 2, 3, or 12 are (1,1), (1,2), (2,1), and (6,6); hence P(2, 3, or 12) $= \frac{1+2+1}{36} = \frac{4}{36} = \frac{1}{9}$.

25.
a. There are 18 odd numbers; hence, P(odd) $= \frac{18}{36} = \frac{9}{19}$.

b. There are 9 numbers greater than 27 (28 through 36) hence, the probability is $\frac{9}{38}$.

c. There are 5 numbers containing the digit 0 hence the probability is $\frac{5}{38}$.

d. The event in part a is most likely to occur since it has the highest probability of occurring.

27.
P(right amount or too little) $= 0.35 + 0.19$
P(right amount or too little) $= 0.54$

29.
a.

|   | 1 | 2 | 3 | 4 | 5 | 6 |
|---|---|---|---|---|---|---|
| 1 | 1 | 2 | 3 | 4 | 5 | 6 |
| 2 | 2 | 4 | 6 | 8 | 10 | 12 |
| 3 | 3 | 6 | 9 | 12 | 15 | 18 |
| 4 | 4 | 8 | 12 | 16 | 20 | 24 |
| 5 | 5 | 10 | 15 | 20 | 25 | 30 |
| 6 | 6 | 12 | 18 | 24 | 30 | 36 |

b. P(multiple of 6) $= \frac{15}{36} = \frac{5}{12}$

c. P(less than 10) $= \frac{17}{36}$

31.

| | | |
|---|---|---|
| | $5 | $1, $5 |
| $1 | $10 | $1, $10 |
| | $20 | $1, $20 |
| | $1 | $5, $1 |
| $5 | $10 | $5, $10 |
| | $20 | $5, $20 |
| | $1 | $10, $1 |
| $10 | $5 | $10, $5 |
| | $20 | $10, $20 |
| | $1 | $20, $1 |
| $20 | $5 | $20, $5 |
| | $10 | $20, $10 |

33.

| | | |
|---|---|---|
| | 1 | 1,1 |
| 1 | 2 | 1,2 |
| | 3 | 1,3 |
| | 4 | 1,4 |
| | 1 | 2,1 |
| 2 | 2 | 2,2 |
| | 3 | 2,3 |
| | 4 | 2,4 |
| | 1 | 3,1 |
| 3 | 2 | 3,2 |
| | 3 | 3,3 |
| | 4 | 3,4 |
| | 1 | 4,1 |
| 4 | 2 | 4,2 |
| | 3 | 4,3 |
| | 4 | 4,4 |

35.

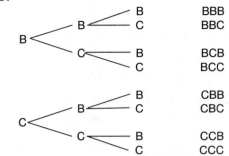

| | | | | |
|---|---|---|---|---|
| | | B | | BBB |
| | B | C | | BBC |
| B | | | | |
| | C | B | | BCB |
| | | C | | BCC |
| | | B | | CBB |
| | B | C | | CBC |
| C | | | | |
| | C | B | | CCB |
| | | C | | CCC |

37.
a. 0.08
b. 0.01
c. $0.08 + 0.27 = 0.35$
d. $0.01 + 0.24 + 0.11 = 0.36$

39.
The statement is probably not based on empirical probability and probably not true.

41.
Actual outcomes will vary, however each number should occur approximately $\frac{1}{6}$ of the time.

43.
a. 1:5, 5:1     e. 1:12, 12:1
b. 1:1, 1:1     f. 1:3, 3:1
c. 1:3, 3:1     g. 1:1, 1:1
d. 1:1, 1:1

EXERCISE SET 4-3

1.
Two events are mutually exclusive if they cannot occur at the same time. Examples will vary.

3.
Using months: P(September or October) $= \frac{2}{12} = \frac{1}{6}$

Using days: P(September or October) $= \frac{61}{365}$

Using days makes the probability slightly larger than using months.

5.
$\frac{4}{19} + \frac{7}{19} = \frac{11}{19}$

7.
a. $\frac{56}{200} = \frac{7}{25}$ or 0.28

7. continued
b. $\frac{75}{200} = \frac{3}{8}$ or 0.375
c. $\frac{34}{200} = \frac{17}{100}$ or 0.17
d. Event b has the highest probability so it is most likely to occur.

9.
P(football or basketball) $=$
$\frac{58 + 40 - 8}{200} = \frac{90}{200}$ or 0.45

P(neither) $= 1 - \frac{90}{200} = \frac{11}{20}$ or 0.55

11.
| | Junior | Senior | Total |
|---|---|---|---|
| Female | 6 | 6 | 12 |
| Male | 12 | 4 | 16 |
| Total | 18 | 10 | 28 |

a. $\frac{18}{28} + \frac{12}{28} - \frac{6}{28} = \frac{24}{28} = \frac{6}{7}$

b. $\frac{10}{28} + \frac{12}{28} - \frac{6}{28} = \frac{16}{28} = \frac{4}{7}$

c. $\frac{18}{28} + \frac{10}{28} = \frac{28}{28} = 1$

13.
| | SUV | Compact | Mid-sized | Total |
|---|---|---|---|---|
| Foreign | 20 | 50 | 20 | 90 |
| Domestic | 65 | 100 | 45 | 210 |
| Total | 85 | 150 | 65 | 300 |

a. P(domestic) $= \frac{210}{300} = \frac{7}{10}$ or 0.7

b. P(foreign and mid-sized) $= \frac{20}{300} = \frac{1}{15} = 0.0667$

c. P(domestic or SUV) $= \frac{210}{300} + \frac{85}{300} - \frac{65}{300}$
$= \frac{230}{300} = \frac{23}{30}$ or 0.7667

15.
| | Cashier | Clerk | Deli | Total |
|---|---|---|---|---|
| Married | 8 | 12 | 3 | 23 |
| Not Married | 5 | 15 | 2 | 22 |
| Total | 13 | 27 | 5 | 45 |

a. P(stock clerk or married) $=$ P(clerk) $+$ P(married) $-$ P(married stock clerk) $=$
$\frac{27}{45} + \frac{23}{45} - \frac{12}{45} = \frac{38}{45}$

b. P(not married) $= \frac{22}{45}$

15. continued

c. P(cashier or not married) = P(cashier) + P(not married) − P(unmarried cashier) $= \frac{13}{45} + \frac{22}{45} - \frac{5}{45} = \frac{30}{45} = \frac{2}{3}$

17.

|  | Ch. 6 | Ch. 8 | Ch. 10 | Total |
|---|---|---|---|---|
| Quiz | 5 | 2 | 1 | 8 |
| Comedy | 3 | 2 | 8 | 13 |
| Drama | 4 | 4 | 2 | 10 |
| Total | 12 | 8 | 11 | 31 |

a. P(quiz show or channel 8) = P(quiz) + P(channel 8) − P(quiz show on ch. 8) = $\frac{8}{31} + \frac{8}{31} - \frac{2}{31} = \frac{14}{31}$

b. P(drama or comedy) = P(drama) + P(comedy) = $\frac{13}{31} + \frac{10}{31} = \frac{23}{31}$

c. P(channel 10 or drama) = P(ch. 10) + P(drama) − P(drama on channel 10) = $\frac{11}{31} + \frac{10}{31} - \frac{2}{31} = \frac{19}{31}$

19.
The total of the frequencies is 30.

a. $\frac{2}{30} = \frac{1}{15}$

b. $\frac{2+3+5}{30} = \frac{10}{30} = \frac{1}{3}$

c. $\frac{12+8+2+3}{30} = \frac{25}{30} = \frac{5}{6}$

d. $\frac{12+8+2+3}{30} = \frac{25}{30} = \frac{5}{6}$

e. $\frac{8+2}{30} = \frac{10}{30} = \frac{1}{3}$

21.
The total of the frequencies is 24.

a. $\frac{10}{24} = \frac{5}{12}$

b. $\frac{2+1}{24} = \frac{3}{24} = \frac{1}{8}$

c. $\frac{10+3+2+1}{24} = \frac{16}{24} = \frac{2}{3}$

d. $\frac{8+10+3+2}{24} = \frac{23}{24}$

23.
a. There are 4 kings, 4 queens, and 4 jacks; hence P(king or queen or jack) = $\frac{12}{52} = \frac{3}{13}$

b. There are 13 clubs, 13 hearts, and 13 spades; hence, P(club or heart or spade) = $\frac{13+13+13}{52} = \frac{39}{52} = \frac{3}{4}$

23. continued

c. There are 4 kings, 4 queens, and 13 diamonds but the king and queen of diamonds were counted twice, hence; P(king or queen or diamond) = P(king) + P(queen) + P(diamond) − P(king and queen of diamonds) = $\frac{4}{52} + \frac{4}{52} + \frac{13}{52} - \frac{2}{52} = \frac{19}{52}$

d. There are 4 aces, 13 diamonds, and 13 hearts. There is one ace of diamonds and one ace of hearts; hence, P(ace or diamond or heart) = P(ace) + P(diamond) + P(heart) − P(ace of hearts and ace of diamonds) = $\frac{4}{52} + \frac{13}{52} + \frac{13}{52} - \frac{2}{52} = \frac{28}{52} = \frac{7}{13}$

e. There are 4 nines, 4 tens, 13 spades, and 13 clubs. There is one nine of spades, one ten of spades, one nine of clubs and one ten of clubs. Hence, P(9 or 10 or spade or club) = P(9) + P(10) + P(spade) + P(club) − P(9 and 10 of clubs and spades) = $\frac{4}{52} + \frac{4}{52} + \frac{13}{52} + \frac{13}{52} - \frac{4}{52} = \frac{30}{52} = \frac{15}{26}$

25.
P(red or white ball) = $\frac{7}{10}$

27.
P(mushrooms or pepperoni) =
          P(mushrooms) + P(pepperoni) −
          P(mushrooms and pepperoni)

Let X = P(mushrooms and pepperoni)
Then 0.55 = 0.32 + 0.17 − X
X = 0.06

29.
P(not a two-car garage) = 1 − 0.70 = 0.30

EXERCISE SET 4-4

1.
a. Independent    e. Independent
b. Dependent      f. Dependent
c. Dependent      g. Dependent
d. Dependent      h. Independent

3.
P(both are women) = $(.84)^2 = 0.706$ or 70.6%
The event is likely to occur since the probability is greater than 0.5.

**5.**
P(male graduate) $= 1 - 0.28 = 0.72$
P(all 3 are male) $= (0.72)^3 = 0.373$ or
37.3%
The event is unlikely to occur since the
probability is less than 0.5.

**7.**
a.  P(no computer) $= 1 - 0.543 = 0.457$
P(none of three has a computer) $=$
$(0.457)^3 = 0.0954$

b.  P(at least one has a computer) $=$
$1 - $ P(none of three has a computer) $=$
$1 - 0.0954 = 0.9046$

c.  P(all three have computers) $=$
$(0.543)^3 = 0.1601$

**9.**
P(all are citizens) $= (0.801)^3 = 0.5139$

**11.**
P(all three have NFL apparel) $=$
$(0.31)^3 = 0.0298$

**13.**
P(no insurance) $= 0.12$
P(none are covered) $= (0.12)^4 = 0.0002$

**15.**
P(5 buy at least 1) $= (\frac{90}{120})^5 = \frac{243}{1024}$

**17.**
$\frac{5}{8} \cdot \frac{4}{7} \cdot \frac{3}{6} = \frac{5}{28}$

**19.**
$\frac{23}{38} \cdot \frac{22}{37} \cdot \frac{21}{36} = \frac{1771}{8436}$ or 0.210

The event is unlikely to occur since the
probability is less than 0.5.

**21.**

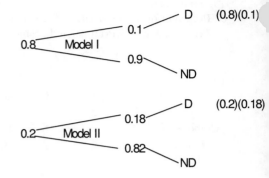

P(defective) $= 0.08 + 0.036 = 0.116$

**23.**

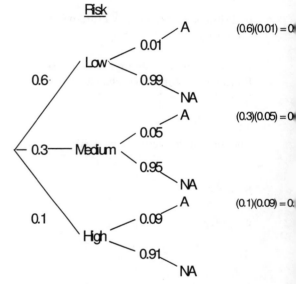

P(accident) $= .006 + .015 + .009 = 0.03$

**25.**
P(red ball) $= \frac{1}{3} \cdot \frac{5}{8} + \frac{1}{3} \cdot \frac{3}{4} + \frac{1}{3} \cdot \frac{4}{6} = \frac{49}{72}$

**27.**
P(auto will be found within one week | it's
been stolen) $= \frac{\text{P(stolen and found within 1 week)}}{\text{P(stolen)}}$
$= \frac{0.0009}{0.0015} = 0.6$

**29.**
P(swim | bridge) $= \frac{\text{P(play bridge and swim)}}{\text{P(play bridge)}}$

$= \frac{0.73}{0.82} = 0.89$ or 89%

31.
P(garage | deck) $= \frac{0.42}{0.60} = 0.7$ or 70%

33.
P(champagne | bridge) $= \frac{0.68}{0.83} = 0.82$ or 82%

35.
a.  P(foreign patent | corporation) =

$\frac{\text{P(corporation and foreign patent)}}{\text{P(corporation)}} =$

$\frac{\frac{63,182}{147,497}}{\frac{134,076}{147,497}} = \frac{63,182}{134,076} = 0.4712$

b.  P(individual | U. S. ) $= \frac{\text{P(U. S. \& individual)}}{\text{P(U. S.)}}$

$\frac{\frac{6129}{147,497}}{\frac{77,944}{147,497}} = \frac{6129}{77,944} = 0.0786$

37.
a.  P(none have been married) $= (0.703)^5 = 0.1717$

b.  P(at least one has been married) =
1 − P(none have been married)
= 1 − 0.1717
= 0.8283

39.
P(at least one not immunized) = 1 − P(none of the six are not immunized)
= 1 − P(all six are immunized)
= 1 − $(0.76)^6 = 0.8073$

41.
If P(read to) = 0.58, then
P(not being read to) = 1 − 0.58 = 0.42

P(at least one is read to) = 1 − P(none are read to)
= 1 − P(all five are not read to)
= 1 − $(0.42)^5 = 0.9869$

43.
P(at least one club) = 1 − P(no clubs)
$1 - \frac{39}{52} \cdot \frac{38}{51} \cdot \frac{37}{50} \cdot \frac{36}{49} = 1 - \frac{6327}{20,825}$
$= \frac{14,498}{20,825}$

45.
P(at least one defective) = 1 − P(no defective) = 1 − $(.94)^5 = 0.266$ or 26.6%

47.
P(at least one tail) = 1 − P(no tails)
$1 - (\frac{1}{2})^5 = 1 - \frac{1}{32} = \frac{31}{32}$

49.
P(at least one 3) = 1 − P(no 3's)
$1 - (\frac{5}{6})^7 = 1 - \frac{78,125}{279,936} = \frac{201,811}{279,936}$ or 0.721
The event is likely to occur since the probability is about 72%.

51.
P(at least one even) = 1 − P(no evens)
$1 - (\frac{1}{2})^3 = 1 - \frac{1}{8} = \frac{7}{8}$

53.
No, because P(A ∩ B) = 0 therefore
P(A ∩ B) ≠ P(A) · P(B)

55.
Yes.

P(enroll) = 0.55

P(enroll | DW) > P(enroll) which indicates that DW has a positive effect on enrollment.

P(enroll | LP) = P(enroll) which indicates that LP has no effect on enrollment.

P(enroll | MH) < P(enroll) which indicates that MH has a low effect on enrollment.

Thus, all students should meet with DW.

EXERCISE SET 4-5

1.
$10^5 = 100,000$
$10 \cdot 9 \cdot 8 \cdot 7 \cdot 6 = 30,240$

3.
$7! = 7 \cdot 6 \cdot 5 \cdot 4 \cdot 3 \cdot 2 \cdot 1 = 5040$

5.
$8! = 8 \cdot 7 \cdot 6 \cdot 5 \cdot 4 \cdot 3 \cdot 2 \cdot 1 = 40,320$

7.
$5! = 5 \cdot 4 \cdot 3 \cdot 2 \cdot 1 = 120$

9.
$10 \cdot 10 \cdot 10 = 1000$
$1 \cdot 9 \cdot 8 = 72$

11.
$$5 \cdot 2 = 10$$

13.
a. $8! = 8 \cdot 7 \cdot 6 \cdot 5 \cdot 4 \cdot 3 \cdot 2 \cdot 1 = 40,320$

b. $10! = 10 \cdot 9 \cdot 8 \cdot 7 \cdot 6 \cdot 5 \cdot 4 \cdot 3 \cdot 2 \cdot 1$
$10! = 3,628,800$

c. $0! = 1$

d. $1! = 1$

e. $_7P_5 = \frac{7!}{(7-5)!}$

$= \frac{7 \cdot 6 \cdot 5 \cdot 4 \cdot 3 \cdot 2 \cdot 1}{2 \cdot 1} = 2520$

f. $_{12}P_4 = \frac{12!}{(12-4)!}$

$= \frac{12 \cdot 11 \cdot 10 \cdot 9 \cdot 8 \cdot 7 \cdot 6 \cdot 5 \cdot 4 \cdot 3 \cdot 2 \cdot 1}{8 \cdot 7 \cdot 6 \cdot 5 \cdot 4 \cdot 3 \cdot 2 \cdot 1} = 11,880$

g. $_5P_3 = \frac{5!}{(5-3)!}$

$= \frac{5 \cdot 4 \cdot 3 \cdot 2 \cdot 1}{2 \cdot 1} = 60$

h. $_6P_0 = \frac{6!}{(6-0)!}$

$= \frac{6 \cdot 5 \cdot 4 \cdot 3 \cdot 2 \cdot 1}{6 \cdot 5 \cdot 4 \cdot 3 \cdot 2 \cdot 1} = 1$

i. $_5P_5 = \frac{5!}{(5-5)!}$

$= \frac{5 \cdot 4 \cdot 3 \cdot 2 \cdot 1}{0!} = 120$

j. $_6P_2 = \frac{6!}{(6-2)!}$

$= \frac{6 \cdot 5 \cdot 4 \cdot 3 \cdot 2 \cdot 1}{4 \cdot 3 \cdot 2 \cdot 1} = 30$

15.
$_4P_4 = \frac{4!}{(4-4)!} = \frac{4 \cdot 3 \cdot 2 \cdot 1}{0!} = 24$

17.
$_6P_3 = \frac{6!}{(6-3)!} = \frac{6!}{3!} = 120$

19.
$_7P_4 = \frac{7!}{(7-4)!} = \frac{7 \cdot 6 \cdot 5 \cdot 4 \cdot 3 \cdot 2 \cdot 1}{3 \cdot 2 \cdot 1} = 840$

21.
$_{10}P_6 = \frac{10!}{(10-6)!} = \frac{10 \cdot 9 \cdot 8 \cdot 7 \cdot 6 \cdot 5 \cdot 4 \cdot 3 \cdot 2 \cdot 1}{4 \cdot 3 \cdot 2 \cdot 1} = 151,200$

23.
$_{50}P_4 = \frac{50!}{(50-4)!} = \frac{50!}{46!} = 5,527,200$

25.
$_5P_3 + _5P_4 + _5P_5 = \frac{5!}{2!} + \frac{5!}{1!} + \frac{5!}{0!}$

$= 60 + 120 + 120 = 300$

27.
a. $\frac{5!}{3! \, 2!} = 10$     f. $\frac{3!}{3! \, 0!} = 1$

b. $\frac{8!}{5! \, 3!} = 56$     g. $\frac{3!}{0! \, 3!} = 1$

c. $\frac{7!}{3! \, 4!} = 35$     h. $\frac{9!}{2! \, 7!} = 36$

d. $\frac{6!}{4! \, 2!} = 15$     i. $\frac{12!}{10! \, 2!} = 66$

e. $\frac{6!}{2! \, 4!} = 15$     j. $\frac{4!}{1! \, 3!} = 4$

29.

$_{10}C_3 = \frac{10!}{7! \, 3!} = \frac{10 \cdot 9 \cdot 8 \cdot 7!}{7! \cdot 3 \cdot 2 \cdot 1} = 120$

31.
$_{10}C_4 = \frac{10!}{6! \, 4!} = 210$

33.
$_{20}C_5 = \frac{20!}{15! \, 5!} = 15,504$

35.
$_{11}C_2 \cdot _8C_3 = 55 \cdot 56 = 3080$

37.
$_{12}C_4 = 495$
$_7C_2 \cdot _5C_2 = 21 \cdot 10 = 210$
$_7C_2 \cdot _5C_2 + _7C_3 \cdot _5C_1 + _7C_4 =$
$21 \cdot 10 + 35 \cdot 5 + 35 =$
$210 + 175 + 35 = 420$

39.
$_6C_3 \cdot _5C_2 = \frac{6!}{3! \, 3!} \cdot \frac{5!}{3! \, 2!}$
$= \frac{6 \cdot 5 \cdot 4 \cdot 3!}{3! \cdot 3 \cdot 2 \cdot 1} \cdot \frac{5 \cdot 4 \cdot 3!}{3! \cdot 2 \cdot 1} = 200$

41.
$_{10}C_2 \cdot _{12}C_2 = \frac{10!}{8! \, 2!} \cdot \frac{12!}{10! \, 2!}$
$= 45 \cdot 66 = 2,970$

43.
$_{17}C_2 = \frac{17!}{15! \, 2!} = 136$

45.
$_{11}C_7 = \frac{11!}{4! \, 7!} = \frac{11 \cdot 10 \cdot 9 \cdot 8 \cdot 7!}{7! \cdot 4 \cdot 3 \cdot 2 \cdot 1} = 330$

47.
$_{20}C_8 = \frac{20!}{12! \, 8!} = \frac{20 \cdot 19 \cdot 18 \cdot 17 \cdot 16 \cdot 15 \cdot 14 \cdot 13 \cdot 12!}{12! \cdot 8 \cdot 7 \cdot 6 \cdot 5 \cdot 4 \cdot 3 \cdot 2 \cdot 1}$
$= 125,970$

**49.**

Selecting 1 coin there are 4 ways. Selecting 2 coins there are 6 ways. Selecting 3 coins there are 4 ways. Selecting 4 coins there is 1 way. Hence the total is $4 + 6 + 4 + 1 = 15$ ways. (List all possibilities.)

**51.**

a. $2 \cdot 4 \cdot 3 \cdot 2 \cdot 1 = 48$

b. $4 \cdot 6 + 3 \cdot 6 + 2 \cdot 6 + 1 \cdot 6 = 60$

c. 72

### EXERCISE SET 4-6

**1.**

$P(2 \text{ face cards}) = \frac{12}{52} \cdot \frac{11}{51} = \frac{11}{221}$

**3.**

a. There are $_4C_3$ ways of selecting 3 women and $_7C_3$ total ways to select 3 people; hence, $P(\text{all women}) = \frac{_4C_3}{_7C_3} = \frac{4}{35}$.

b. There are $_3C_3$ ways of selecting 3 men; hence, $P(\text{all men}) = \frac{_3C_3}{_7C_3} = \frac{1}{35}$.

c. There are $_3C_2$ ways of selecting 2 men and $_4C_1$ ways of selecting one woman; hence, $P(2 \text{ men and 1 woman}) = \frac{_3C_2 \cdot _4C_1}{_7C_3} = \frac{12}{35}$.

d. There are $_3C_1$ ways to select one man and $_4C_2$ ways of selecting two women; hence, $P(1 \text{ man and 2 women}) = \frac{_3C_1 \cdot _4C_2}{_7C_3} = \frac{18}{35}$.

**5.**

a. There are $_9C_4$ ways to select four from Pennsylvania; hence $P(\text{all four are from Pennsylvania}) = \frac{_9C_4}{_{56}C_4} = \frac{126}{367,290} = 0.0003$

b. There are $_9C_2$ ways to select two from Pennsylvania and $_7C_2$ ways to select two from Virginia; hence $P(\text{two from Pennsylvania and two from Virginia}) = \frac{_9C_2 \cdot _7C_2}{_{56}C_4} = \frac{756}{367,290} = 0.0021$

**7.**

$\frac{2}{50} \cdot \frac{1}{49} = \frac{1}{1225}$

**9.**

a. $\frac{_8C_4}{_{14}C_4} = \frac{70}{1001} = \frac{10}{143}$

b. $\frac{_6C_2 \cdot _8C_2}{_{14}C_4} = \frac{420}{1001} = \frac{60}{143}$

**7. continued**

c. $\frac{_6C_4}{_{14}C_4} = \frac{15}{1001}$

d. $\frac{_6C_3 \cdot _8C_1}{_{14}C_4} = \frac{160}{1001}$

e. $\frac{_6C_1 \cdot _8C_3}{_{14}C_4} = \frac{336}{1001} = \frac{48}{143}$

**11.**

a. $\frac{_{11}C_2}{_{19}C_2} = \frac{55}{171} = 0.3216$

b. $\frac{_8C_2}{_{19}C_2} = \frac{28}{171} = 0.1637$

c. $\frac{_{11}C_1 \cdot _8C_1}{_{19}C_2} = \frac{88}{171} = 0.5146$

d. It probably got lost in the wash!

**13.**

There are $6^3 = 216$ ways of tossing three dice, and there are 15 ways of getting a sum of 7; i.e., (1, 1, 5), (1, 5, 1), (5, 1, 1), (1, 2, 4), etc. Hence the probability of rolling a sum of 7 is $\frac{15}{216} = \frac{5}{72}$.

**15.**

There are $5! = 120$ ways to arrange 5 washers in a row and 2 ways to have them in correct order, small to large or large to small; hence, the probability is $\frac{2}{120} = \frac{1}{60}$.

### REVIEW EXERCISES - CHAPTER 4

**1.**

a. $\frac{1}{6}$    b. $\frac{1}{6}$    c. $\frac{4}{6} = \frac{2}{3}$

**3.**

$\frac{16}{45}$

**5.**

$\frac{850}{1500} = \frac{17}{30}$

**7.**

a. $\frac{3}{30} = \frac{1}{10}$    c. $\frac{16+7+3}{30} = \frac{26}{30} = \frac{13}{15}$

b. $\frac{7+4}{30} = \frac{11}{30}$    d. $1 - \frac{4}{30} = \frac{26}{30} = \frac{13}{15}$

**9.**

$0.80 + 0.30 - 0.12 = 0.98$

**11.**

$(0.78)^5 = 0.289 \text{ or } 28.9\%$

13.

a. $\frac{26}{52} \cdot \frac{25}{51} \cdot \frac{24}{50} = \frac{2}{17}$

b. $\frac{13}{52} \cdot \frac{12}{51} \cdot \frac{11}{50} = \frac{33}{2550} = \frac{11}{850}$

c. $\frac{4}{52} \cdot \frac{3}{51} \cdot \frac{2}{50} = \frac{1}{5525}$

15.

$P(C \text{ or } PP) = P(C) + P(PP) = \frac{2+3}{13} = \frac{5}{13}$

17.

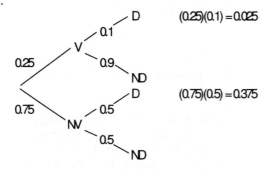

$P(\text{disease}) = 0.025 + 0.375 = 0.4$

19.

$P(NC \mid C) = \frac{P(NC \text{ and } C)}{P(C)} = \frac{0.37}{0.73} = 0.51$

21.

$\frac{0.43}{0.75} = 0.573$ or 57.3%

23.

|  | <4 yrs HS | HS | College | Total |
|---|---|---|---|---|
| Smoker | 6 | 14 | 19 | 39 |
| Non-Smoker | 18 | 7 | 25 | 50 |
| Total | 24 | 21 | 44 | 89 |

a. There are 44 college graduates and 19 of them smoke; hence, the probability is $\frac{19}{44}$.

b. There are 24 people who did not graduate from high school, 6 of whom do not smoke; hence, the probability is
$\frac{6}{24} = \frac{1}{4}$.

25.

P(at least one tail) = 1 − P(all heads)
$1 - \left(\frac{1}{2}\right)^5 = 1 - \frac{1}{32} = \frac{31}{32}$

27.

If repetitions are allowed:
$26 \cdot 26 \cdot 26 \cdot 10 \cdot 10 \cdot 10 = 175,760,000$

27. continued

If repetitions are not allowed:
$_{26}P_3 \cdot _{10}P_4 = \frac{26 \cdot 25 \cdot 24 \cdot 23!}{23!} \cdot \frac{10 \cdot 9 \cdot 8 \cdot 7 \cdot 6!}{6!}$
$= 78,624,000$

If repetitions are allowed in the letters but not in the digits:
$26 \cdot 26 \cdot 26 \cdot _{10}P_4 = 88,583,040$

29.

$_5C_3 \cdot _7C_4 = \frac{5!}{2! \, 3!} \cdot \frac{7!}{3! \, 4!} = 10 \cdot 35 = 350$

31.

$_{10}C_2 = \frac{10!}{8! \, 2!} = 45$

33.

$26 \cdot 10 \cdot 10 \cdot 10 = 26,000$

35.

$_{12}C_4 = \frac{12!}{8! \, 4!} = \frac{12 \cdot 11 \cdot 10 \cdot 9 \cdot 8!}{4 \cdot 3 \cdot 2 \cdot 1 \cdot 8!} = 495$

37.

$_{20}C_5 = \frac{20!}{15! \, 5!} = \frac{20 \cdot 19 \cdot 18 \cdot 17 \cdot 16 \cdot 15!}{15! \, 5 \cdot 4 \cdot 3 \cdot 2 \cdot 1} = 15,504$

39.

Total number of outcomes:
$26 \cdot 26 \cdot 26 \cdot 10 \cdot 10 \cdot 10 \cdot 10 = 175,760,000$

Total number of ways for USA followed by a number divisible by 5:
$1 \cdot 1 \cdot 1 \cdot 10 \cdot 10 \cdot 10 \cdot 2 = 2000$

Hence $P = \frac{2000}{175,760,000} = 0.0000114$

41.

$\frac{_3C_1 \cdot _4C_1 \cdot _2C_1}{_9C_3} = \frac{2}{7}$

## CHAPTER 4 QUIZ

1. False, subjective probability can be used when other types of probabilities cannot be found.
2. False, empirical probability uses frequency distributions.
3. True
4. False, P(A or B) = P(A) + P(B) − P(A and B)
5. False, the probabilities can be different.
6. False, complementary events cannot occur at the same time.
7. True
8. False, order does not matter in combinations.

9. b

10. b and d

11. d

12. b

13. c

14. b

15. d

16. b

17. b

18. Sample space

19. Zero and one

20. Zero

21. One

22. Mutually exclusive

23. a. $\frac{4}{52} = \frac{1}{13}$     c. $\frac{16}{52} = \frac{4}{13}$

    b. $\frac{4}{52} = \frac{1}{13}$

24. a. $\frac{13}{52} = \frac{1}{4}$     d. $\frac{4}{52} = \frac{1}{13}$

    b. $\frac{4+13-1}{52} = \frac{4}{13}$   e. $\frac{26}{52} = \frac{1}{2}$

    c. $\frac{1}{52}$

25. a. $\frac{12}{31}$     c. $\frac{27}{31}$

    b. $\frac{12}{31}$     d. $\frac{24}{31}$

26. a. $\frac{11}{36}$     d. $\frac{1}{3}$

    b. $\frac{5}{18}$     e. 0

    c. $\frac{11}{36}$     f. $\frac{11}{12}$

27. $(0.75 - 0.16) + (0.25 - 0.16) = 0.68$

28. $(0.3)^5 = 0.002$

29. a. $\frac{26}{52} \cdot \frac{25}{51} \cdot \frac{24}{50} \cdot \frac{23}{49} \cdot \frac{22}{48} = \frac{253}{9996}$

    b. $\frac{13}{52} \cdot \frac{12}{51} \cdot \frac{11}{50} \cdot \frac{10}{49} \cdot \frac{9}{48} = \frac{33}{66,640}$

    c. 0

30. $\frac{0.35}{0.65} = 0.54$

31. $\frac{0.16}{0.3} = 0.53$

32. $\frac{0.57}{0.7} = 0.81$

33. $\frac{0.028}{0.5} = 0.056$

34. a. $\frac{1}{2}$     b. $\frac{3}{7}$

35. $1 - (0.45)^6 = 0.99$

36. $1 - (\frac{5}{6})^4 = 0.518$

37. $1 - (0.15)^6 = 0.9999886$

38. 2,646

39. 40,320

40. 1,365

41. 1,188,137,600; 710,424,000

42. 720

43. 33,554,432

44. 56

45. $\frac{1}{4}$

46. $\frac{3}{14}$

47. $\frac{12}{55}$

48.

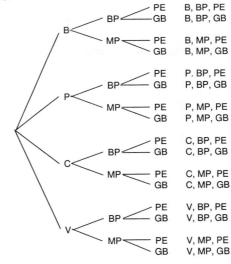

Note: Answers may vary due to rounding,
TI-83's or computer programs.

EXERCISE SET 5-2

1.
A random variable is a variable whose
values are determined by chance. Examples
will vary.

3.
The number of commercials a radio station
plays during each hour.
The number of times a student uses his or
her calculator during a mathematics exam.
The number of leaves on a specific type of
tree.

5.
A probability distribution is a distribution
which consists of the values a random
variable can assume along with the
corresponding probabilities of these values.

7.
No; probabilities cannot be negative and the
sum of the probabilities is not one.

9.
Yes

11.
No, probability values cannot be greater than
1.

13.
Discrete

15.
Continuous

17.
Discrete

19.

| X | 0 | 1 | 2 | 3 |
|------|------|------|------|------|
| P(X) | $\frac{6}{15}$ | $\frac{5}{15}$ | $\frac{3}{15}$ | $\frac{1}{15}$ |

19. continued

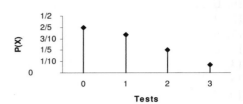
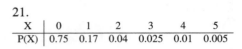

Tests

21.

| X | 0 | 1 | 2 | 3 | 4 | 5 |
|------|------|------|------|------|------|------|
| P(X) | 0.75 | 0.17 | 0.04 | 0.025 | 0.01 | 0.005 |

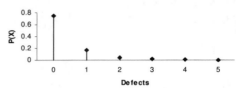
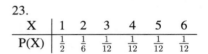

Defects

23.

| X | 1 | 2 | 3 | 4 | 5 | 6 |
|------|------|------|------|------|------|------|
| P(X) | $\frac{1}{2}$ | $\frac{1}{6}$ | $\frac{1}{12}$ | $\frac{1}{12}$ | $\frac{1}{12}$ | $\frac{1}{12}$ |

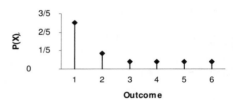

Outcome

25.

| X | 3 | 4 | 5 | 6 | 7 |
|------|------|------|------|------|------|
| P(X) | 0.15 | 0.20 | 0.25 | 0.2 | 0.2 |

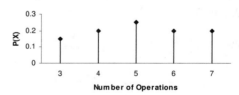
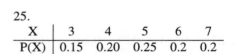

Number of Operations

27.

| X | $1 | $5 | $10 | $20 |
|------|------|------|------|------|
| P(X) | $\frac{2}{9}$ | $\frac{1}{3}$ | $\frac{1}{9}$ | $\frac{1}{3}$ |

**27. continued**

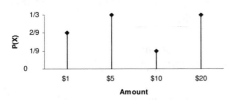

**29.**

| X | 1 | 2 | 3 | 4 |
|---|---|---|---|---|
| P(X) | $\frac{1}{4}$ | $\frac{1}{4}$ | $\frac{3}{8}$ | $\frac{1}{8}$ |

**31.**

| X | 1 | 2 | 3 |
|---|---|---|---|
| P(X) | $\frac{1}{6}$ | $\frac{1}{3}$ | $\frac{1}{2}$ |

Yes.

**33.**

| X | 3 | 4 | 7 |
|---|---|---|---|
| P(X) | $\frac{3}{6}$ | $\frac{4}{6}$ | $\frac{7}{6}$ |

No, the sum of the probabilities is greater than one and $P(7) = \frac{7}{6}$ which is also greater than one.

**35.**

| X | 1 | 2 | 4 |
|---|---|---|---|
| P(X) | $\frac{1}{7}$ | $\frac{2}{7}$ | $\frac{4}{7}$ |

Yes.

**EXERCISE SET 5-3**

**1.**

| X | 0 | 1 | 2 | 3 |
|---|---|---|---|---|
| P(X) | 0.92 | 0.03 | 0.03 | 0.02 |

$\mu = \sum X \cdot P(X) = 0(0.92) + 1(0.03) +$

$2(0.03) + 3(0.02) = 0.15$ or 0.2

$\sigma^2 = \sum X^2 \cdot P(X) - \mu^2 = [0^2(0.92) +$
$1^2(0.03) + 2^2(0.03) + 3^2(0.02)] - 0.15^2 =$
0.3075

$\sigma = \sqrt{0.3075} = 0.55$ or 0.6

The company would need $0.2(10) = 2$ extra transistors on hand each day.

**1. continued**

| X | P(X) | $X \cdot P(X)$ | $X^2 \cdot P(X)$ |
|---|---|---|---|
| 0 | 0.92 | 0 | 0 |
| 1 | 0.03 | 0.03 | 0.03 |
| 2 | 0.03 | 0.06 | 0.12 |
| 3 | 0.02 | 0.06 | 0.18 |
| | | $\mu = 0.15$ | 0.33 |

**3.**
$\mu = \sum X \cdot P(X) = 0(0.18) + 1(0.44) +$
$2(0.27) + 3(0.08) + 4(0.03) = 1.34$ or 1.3

$\sigma^2 = \sum X^2 \cdot P(X) - \mu^2 = [0^2(0.18) +$
$1^2(0.44) + 2^2(0.27) + 3^2(0.08) + 4^2(0.03)]$
$- 1.34^2 = 0.92$ or 0.9

$\sigma = \sqrt{0.92} = 0.96$ or 1

No, on average each person has about one credit card.

| X | P(X) | $X \cdot P(X)$ | $X^2 \cdot P(X)$ |
|---|---|---|---|
| 0 | 0.18 | 0 | 0 |
| 1 | 0.44 | 0.44 | 0.44 |
| 2 | 0.27 | 0.54 | 1.08 |
| 3 | 0.08 | 0.24 | 0.72 |
| 4 | 0.03 | 0.12 | 0.48 |
| | | $\mu = 1.34$ | 2.72 |

**5.**
$\mu = \sum X \cdot P(X) = 0(0.06) + 1(0.42) +$
$2(0.22) + 3(0.12) + 4(0.15) + 5(0.03)$
$= 1.97$ or 2.0

$\sigma^2 = \sum X^2 \cdot P(X) - \mu^2 = [0^2(0.06) +$
$1^2(0.42) + 2^2(0.22) + 3^2(0.12) + 4^2(0.15)$
$+ 5^2(0.03)] - 1.97^2 = 1.649$ or 1.6

$\sigma = \sqrt{1.649} = 1.28$ or 1.3

| X | P(X) | $X \cdot P(X)$ | $X^2 \cdot P(X)$ |
|---|---|---|---|
| 0 | 0.06 | 0.00 | 0.00 |
| 1 | 0.42 | 0.42 | 0.42 |
| 2 | 0.22 | 0.44 | 0.88 |
| 3 | 0.12 | 0.36 | 1.08 |
| 4 | 0.15 | 0.60 | 2.40 |
| 5 | 0.03 | 0.15 | 0.75 |
| | | $\mu = 1.97$ | 5.53 |

She would average $200 per week.

**7.**
$\mu = \sum X \cdot P(X) = 5(0.2) + 6(0.25) +$
$7(0.38) + 8(0.10) + 9(0.07) = 6.59$ or 6.6

7. continued
$\sigma^2 = \sum X^2 \cdot P(X) - \mu^2 = [5^2(0.2) + 6^2(0.25) + 7^2(0.38) + 8^2(0.10) + 9^2(0.07) - 6.59^2 = 1.2619$ or 1.3

$\sigma = \sqrt{1.2619} = $ `1.123 or 1.1

| X | P(X) | X · P(X) | X² · P(X) |
|---|------|----------|-----------|
| 5 | 0.20 | 1.00 | 5.00 |
| 6 | 0.25 | 1.50 | 9.00 |
| 7 | 0.38 | 2.66 | 18.62 |
| 8 | 0.10 | 0.80 | 6.40 |
| 9 | 0.07 | 0.63 | 5.67 |
|   |      | $\mu = 6.59$ | 44.69 |

9.
$\mu = \sum X \cdot P(X) = 12(0.15) + 13(0.20) + 14(0.38) + 15(0.18) + 16(0.09) = 13.86$ or 13.9

$\sigma^2 = \sum X^2 \cdot P(X) - \mu^2 = [12^2(0.15) + 13^2(0.20) + 14^2(0.38) + 15^2(0.18) + 16^2(0.09)] - 13.86^2 = 1.3204$ or 1.3

$\sigma = \sqrt{1.3204} = 1.1491$ or 1.1

| X | P(X) | X · P(X) | X² · P(X) |
|----|------|----------|-----------|
| 12 | 0.15 | 1.80 | 21.60 |
| 13 | 0.20 | 2.60 | 33.80 |
| 14 | 0.38 | 5.32 | 74.48 |
| 15 | 0.18 | 2.70 | 40.50 |
| 16 | 0.09 | 1.44 | 23.04 |
|    |      | $\mu = 13.86$ | 193.42 |

11.
$E(X) = \sum X \cdot P(X) = \$300(0.998) - \$19,700(0.002) = \$260$

13.
$E(X) = \sum X \cdot P(X) = \$5.00(\frac{1}{6}) = \$0.83$
He should pay about $0.83.

15.
$E(X) = \sum X \cdot P(X) = \$1000(\frac{1}{1000}) + \$500(\frac{1}{1000}) + \$100(\frac{5}{1000}) - \$3.00$
$= -\$1.00$

Alternate Solution:
$E(X) = 997(\frac{1}{1000}) + 497(\frac{1}{1000}) + 97(\frac{5}{1000}) - 3(\frac{993}{1000}) = -\$1.00$

17.
$E(X) = \sum X \cdot P(X) = \$500(\frac{1}{1000}) - \$1.00$
$= -\$0.50$

Alternate Solution:
$E(X) = \$499(\frac{1}{1000}) - 1(\frac{999}{1000}) = -\$0.50$

There are 6 possibilities when a number with all different digits is boxed, $(3 \cdot 2 \cdot 1 = 6)$. Hence,
$\$80.00 \cdot \frac{6}{1000} - \$1.00 = \$0.48 - \$1.00$
$= -\$0.52$

Alternate Solution:
$E(X) = 79(\frac{6}{1000}) - 1(\frac{994}{1000}) = -\$0.52$

19.
$E(X) = \sum X \cdot P(X) = \$80,000(0.2) + \$40,000(0.7) - \$50,000(0.1) = \$39,000$
Yes.

21.
The expected value for a single die is 3.5, and since 3 die are rolled, the expected value is $3(3.5) = 10.5$

23.
Answers will vary.

25.
Answers will vary.

EXERCISE SET 5-4

1.
a. Yes
b. Yes
c. Yes
d. No, there are more than two outcomes.
e. No, there are more than two outcomes.
f. Yes
g. Yes
h. Yes
i. No, there are more than two outcomes.
j. Yes

2.
a. 0.420
b. 0.346
c. 0.590
d. 0.251
e. 0.000
f. 0.250
g. 0.418

2. continued
h. 0.176
i. 0.246

3.
a. $P(X) = \frac{n!}{(n-X)! \, X!} \cdot p^X \cdot q^{n-X}$

$P(X) = \frac{6!}{3! \cdot 3!} \cdot (0.03)^3 (0.97)^3 = 0.0005$

b. $P(X) = \frac{4!}{2! \cdot 2!} \cdot (0.18)^2 \cdot (0.82)^2 = 0.131$

c. $P(X) = \frac{5!}{2! \cdot 3!} = (0.63)^3 \cdot (0.37)^2 = 0.342$

d. $P(X) = \frac{9!}{9! \cdot 0!} \cdot (0.42)^0 \cdot (0.58)^9 = 0.007$

e. $P(X) = \frac{10!}{5! \cdot 5!} \cdot (0.37)^5 \cdot (0.63)^5 = 0.173$

5.
$n = 20, p = 0.5, X \geq 15$
$P(X) = 0.015 + 0.005 + 0.001 = 0.021$
No, it's only about a 2% chance.

7.
$n = 9, p = 0.30, X = 3$
$P(X) = 0.267$

9.
$n = 7, p = 0.75, X = 0, 1, 2, 3$

$P(X) = \frac{7!}{7! \, 0!}(0.75)^0 (0.25)^7 +$

$\frac{7!}{6! \, 1!}(0.75)^1 (0.25)^6 + \frac{7!}{5! \, 2!}(0.75)^2 (0.25)^5 +$

$\frac{7!}{4! \, 3!}(0.75)^3 (0.25)^4 = 0.071$

11.
$n = 5, p = 0.40$
a. $X = 2, P(X) = 0.346$
b. $X = 0, 1, 2,$ or 3 people
$P(X) = 0.078 + 0.259 + 0.346 + 0.230$
$= 0.913$
c. $X = 2, 3, 4,$ or 5 people
$P(X) = 0.346 + 0.230 + 0.077 + 0.01$
$= 0.663$
d. $X = 0, 1,$ or 2 people
$P(X) = 0.683$

13.
a. $n = 10, p = 0.8, X = 0, 1, 2, 3, 4, 5, 6$
$P(X) = 0.001 + 0.006 + 0.026 + 0.088 = 0.121$
b. $n = 10, p = 0.8, X = 6, P(X) = 0.088$

13. continued
c. $n = 10, p = 0.8, X = 6, 7, 8, 9, 10$
$P(X) = 0.088 + 0.201 + 0.302 + 0.268 + 0.107 = 0.966$ (TI83 answer $= 0.967$)
d. Event c is most likely to occur since it has the highest probability.

14.
a. $\mu = 100(0.75) = 75$
$\sigma^2 = 100(0.75)(0.25) = 18.75$ or 18.8
$\sigma = \sqrt{18.75} = 4.33$ or 4.3
b. $\mu = 300(0.3) = 90$
$\sigma^2 = 300(0.3)(0.7) = 63$
$\sigma = \sqrt{63} = 7.94$ or 7.9
c. $\mu = 20(0.5) = 10$
$\sigma^2 = 20(0.5)(0.5) = 5$
$\sigma = \sqrt{5} = 2.236$ or 2.2
d. $\mu = 10(0.8) = 8$
$\sigma^2 = 10(0.8)(0.2) = 1.6$
$\sigma = \sqrt{1.6} = 1.265$ or 1.3
e. $\mu = 1000(0.1) = 100$
$\sigma^2 = 1000(0.1)(0.9) = 90$
$\sigma = \sqrt{90} = 9.49$ or 9.5
f. $\mu = 500(0.25) = 125$
$\sigma^2 = 500(0.25)(0.75) = 93.75$ or 93.8
$\sigma = \sqrt{93.75} = 9.68$ or 9.7
g. $\mu = 50(\frac{2}{5}) = 20$
$\sigma^2 = 50(\frac{2}{5})(\frac{3}{5}) = 12$
$\sigma = \sqrt{12} = 3.464$ or 3.5
h. $\mu = 36(\frac{1}{6}) = 6$
$\sigma^2 = 36(\frac{1}{6})(\frac{5}{6}) = 5$
$\sigma = \sqrt{5} = 2.236$ or 2.2

15.
$n = 800, p = 0.01$
$\mu = 800(0.01) = 8$
$\sigma^2 = 800(0.01)(0.99) = 7.9$
$\sigma = \sqrt{7.92} = 2.8$

17.
$n = 300, p = 0.03$
$\mu = 300(0.03) = 9$
$\sigma^2 = 300(0.03)(0.97) = 8.73$
$\sigma = \sqrt{8.73} = 2.95$

19.
$n = 1000, p = 0.21$
$\mu = 1000(0.21) = 210$
$\sigma^2 = 1000(0.21)(0.79) = 165.9$
$\sigma = \sqrt{165.9} = 12.9$

21.
n = 18, p = 0.25, X = 5
$P(X) = \frac{18!}{13! \, 5!}(0.25)^5(0.75)^{13} = 0.199$

23.
n = 10, p = $\frac{1}{3}$, X = 0, 1, 2, 3
$P(X) = \frac{10!}{10! \, 0!}(\frac{1}{3})^0(\frac{2}{3})^{10} + \frac{10!}{9! \, 1!}(\frac{1}{3})^1(\frac{2}{3})^9$
$+ \frac{10!}{8! \, 2!}(\frac{1}{3})^2(\frac{2}{3})^8 + \frac{10!}{7! \, 3!}(\frac{1}{3})^3(\frac{2}{3})^7 = 0.559$

25.
n = 5, p = 0.13, X = 3, 4, 5
$P(X) = \frac{5!}{2! \, 3!}(0.13)^3(0.87)^2 +$
$\frac{5!}{1! \, 4!}(0.13)^4(0.87)^1 + \frac{5!}{0! \, 5!}(0.13)^5(0.87)^0$
$= 0.018$

27.
n = 12, p = 0.86, X = 10, 11, 12
$P(X) = \frac{12!}{2! \, 10!}(0.86)^{10}(0.14)^2 +$
$\frac{12!}{1! \, 11!}(0.86)^{11}(0.14)^1 + \frac{12!}{0! \, 12!}(0.86)^{12}(0.14)^0$
$= 0.7697$ or 0.770

Yes. The probability is high, 77%.

29.
n = 4, p = 0.3, X = 0, 1, 2, 3, 4

| X | 0 | 1 | 2 | 3 | 4 |
|---|---|---|---|---|---|
| P(X) | 0.240 | 0.412 | 0.265 | 0.076 | 0.008 |

REVIEW EXERCISES - CHAPTER 5

1.
Yes.

3.
No, the sum of the probabilities is greater than one.

5.

| X | 0 | 1 | 2 | 3 | 4 |
|---|---|---|---|---|---|
| P(X) | 0.05 | 0.30 | 0.45 | 0.12 | 0.08 |

5. continued

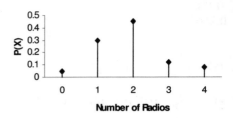

7.

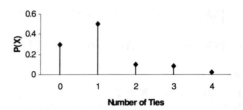

9.
$\mu = \sum X \cdot P(X) = 13(0.12) + 14(0.15) + 15(0.29) + 16(0.25) + 17(0.19) = 15.24$ or 15.2

$\sigma^2 = \sum X^2 \cdot P(X) - \mu^2 = [13^2(0.12) + 14^2(0.15) + 15^2(0.29) + 16^2(0.25) + 17^2(0.19)] - 15.24^2 = 1.5824$ or 1.6

$\sigma = \sqrt{1.5824} = 1.26$ or 1.3

| X | P(X) | $X \cdot P(X)$ | $X^2 \cdot P(X)$ |
|---|---|---|---|
| 13 | 0.12 | 1.56 | 20.28 |
| 14 | 0.15 | 2.1 | 29.4 |
| 15 | 0.29 | 4.35 | 65.25 |
| 16 | 0.25 | 4 | 64 |
| 17 | 0.19 | 3.23 | 54.91 |
|   |   | $\mu = 15.24$ | 233.84 |

11.
$\mu = \sum X \cdot P(X) = 22(0.08) + 23(0.19) + 24(0.36) + 25(0.25) + 26(0.07) + 27(0.05) = 24.19$ or 24.2

$\sigma^2 = \sum X^2 \cdot P(X) - \mu^2 = [22^2(0.08) + 23^2(0.19) + 24^2(0.36) + 25^2(0.25) + 26^2(0.07) + 27^2(0.05)] - 24.19^2 = 1.4539$ or 1.5

$\sigma = \sqrt{1.4539} = 1.206$ or 1.2

# Chapter 5 - Discrete Probability Distributions

11. continued

| X | P(X) | X · P(X) | X² · P(X) |
|---|------|----------|-----------|
| 22 | 0.08 | 1.76 | 38.72 |
| 23 | 0.19 | 4.37 | 100.51 |
| 24 | 0.36 | 8.64 | 207.36 |
| 25 | 0.25 | 6.25 | 156.25 |
| 26 | 0.07 | 1.82 | 47.32 |
| 27 | 0.05 | 1.35 | 36.45 |
| | $\mu =$ | 24.19 | 586.61 |

13.

$\mu = \sum X \cdot P(X)$

$= \frac{1}{2}(\$1.00) + \frac{18}{52}(\$5.00) + \frac{6}{52}(\$10.00) +$

$\frac{2}{52}(\$100.00) = \$7.23$

To break even, a person should bet $7.23.

15.

a. 0.122

b. $1 - 0.002 + 0.009 = 0.989$

c. $0.002 + 0.009 + 0.032 = 0.043$

17.

$\mu = n \cdot p = 180(0.75) = 135$

$\sigma^2 = n \cdot p \cdot q = 180(0.75)(0.25) = 33.75$ or 33.8

$\sigma = \sqrt{33.75} = 5.809$ or 5.8

19.

$n = 8, p = 0.25$

$P(X \le 3) = \frac{8!}{8!\,0!}(0.25)^0(0.75)^8 +$

$\frac{8!}{7!\,1!}(0.25)^1(0.75)^7 + \frac{8!}{6!\,2!}(0.25)^2(0.75)^6 +$

$\frac{8!}{5!\,3!}(0.25)^3(0.75)^5 = 0.8862$ or 0.886

21.

$n = 20, p = 0.75, X = 16$

P(16 have eaten pizza for breakfast) =

$\frac{20!}{4!\,16!}(0.75)^{16}(0.25)^4 = 0.1897$ or 0.190

## CHAPTER 5 QUIZ

1. True
2. False, it is a discrete random variable.
3. False, the outcomes must be independent.
4. True
5. chance
6. $\mu = n \cdot p$
7. one
8. c
9. c
10. d

---

11. No, the sum of the probabilities is greater than one.
12. Yes
13. Yes
14. Yes
15.

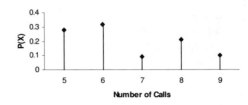

16.

| X | 0 | 1 | 2 | 3 | 4 |
|------|------|------|------|------|------|
| P(X) | 0.02 | 0.30 | 0.48 | 0.13 | 0.07 |

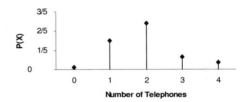

17.

$\mu = 0(0.10) + 1(0.23) + 2(0.31) + 3(0.27)$

$+ 4(0.09) = 2.02$ or 2

$\sigma^2 = [0^2(0.10) + 1^2(0.23) + 2^2(0.31) +$

$3^2(0.27) + 4^2(0.09)] - 2.02^2 = 1.3$

$\sigma = \sqrt{1.3} = 1.1$

18.

$\mu = 30(0.05) + 31(0.21) + 32(0.38) +$

$33(0.25) + 34(0.11) = 32.16$ or 32.2

$\sigma^2 = [30^2(0.05) + 31^2(0.21) + 32^2(0.38) +$

$33^2(0.25) + 34^2(0.11)] - 32.16^2 = 1.07$ or 1.1

$\sigma = \sqrt{1.07} = 1.0$

19.

$\mu = 4(\frac{1}{6}) + 5(\frac{1}{6}) + 2(\frac{1}{6}) + 10(\frac{1}{6}) + 3(\frac{1}{6})$

$+ 7(\frac{1}{6}) = 5.17$ or 5.2

20.

$\mu = \$2(\frac{1}{2}) + \$10(\frac{5}{26}) + \$25(\frac{3}{26}) +$

$\$100(\frac{1}{26}) = \$9.65$

21.

$n = 20, p = 0.40, X = 5$

$P(5) = 0.124$

45

22.
n = 20, p = 0.60
a.  P(15) = 0.075
b.  P(10, 11, ..., 20) = 0.872
c.  P(0, 1, 2, 3, 4, 5) = 0.125

23.
n = 300, p = 0.80
$\mu = 300(0.80) = 240$
$\sigma^2 = 300(0.80)(0.20) = 48$
$\sigma = \sqrt{48} = 6.9$

24.
n = 75, p = 0.12
$\mu = 75(0.12) = 9$
$\sigma^2 = 75(0.12)(0.88) = 7.9$
$\sigma = \sqrt{7.9} = 2.8$

Note: Graphs are not to scale and are intended to convey a general idea.

Answers are generated using Table E. Answers generated using the TI-83 will vary slightly.

EXERCISE SET 6-3

1.
The characteristics of the normal distribution are:
1. It is bell-shaped.
2. It is symmetric about the mean.
3. The mean, median, and mode are equal.
4. It is continuous.
5. It never touches the X-axis.
6. The area under the curve is equal to one.
7. It is unimodal.

3.
One or 100%.

5.
68%, 95%, 99.7%

7.
The area is found by looking up $z = 0.75$ in Table E as shown in Block 1 of Procedure Table 6. Area $= 0.2734$

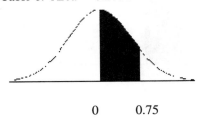

0        0.75

9.
The area is found by looking up $z = 2.07$ in Table E as shown in Block 1 of Procedure Table 6. Area $= 0.4808$

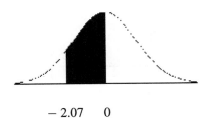

$-2.07$    0

11.
The area is found by looking up $z = 0.23$ in Table E and subtracting it from 0.5 as shown in Block 2 of Procedure Table 6.
$0.5 - 0.0910 = 0.4090$

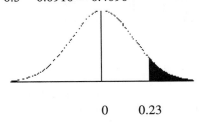

0        0.23

13.
The area is found by looking up $z = 1.43$ in Table E and subtracting it from 0.5 as shown in Block 2 of Procedure Table 6.
$0.5 - 0.4236 = 0.0764$

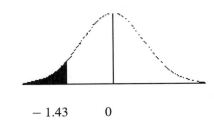

$-1.43$       0

15.
The area is found by looking up the values 0.79 and 1.28 in Table E and subtracting the areas as shown in Block 3 of Procedure Table 6.   $0.3997 - 0.2852 = 0.1145$

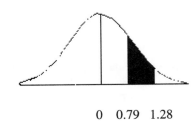

0    0.79   1.28

17.
The area is found by looking up the values 1.56 and 1.83 in Table E and subtracting the areas as shown in Block 3 of Procedure Table 6.    $0.4664 - 0.4406 = 0.0258$

17. continued

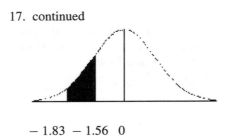

− 1.83 − 1.56  0

19.
The area is found by looking up the values 2.47 and 1.03 in Table E and adding them together as shown in Block 4 of Procedure Table 6.    $0.3485 + 0.4932 = 0.8417$

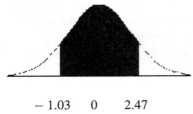

− 1.03    0    2.47

21.
The area is found by looking up $z = 2.11$ in Table E, then adding the area to 0.5 as shown in Block 5 of Procedure Table 6.
$0.5 + 0.4826 = 0.9826$

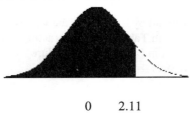

0    2.11

23.
The area is found by looking up $z = 0.15$ in Table E and adding it to 0.5 as shown in Block 6 of Procedure Table 6.
$0.5 + 0.0596 = 0..5596$

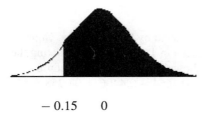

− 0.15    0

25.
The area is found by looking up the values 1.92 and 0.44 in Table E, subtracting both areas from 0.5, and adding them together as shown in Block 7 of Procedure Table 6.

25. continued
$0.5 − 0.4726 = 0.0274$
$0.5 − 0.1700 = 0.3300$
$0.0274 + 0.3300 = 0.3574$

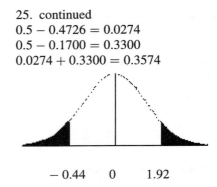

− 0.44    0    1.92

27.
The area is found by looking up $z = 0.67$ in Table E as shown in Block 1 of Procedure Table 6.  Area = 0.2486

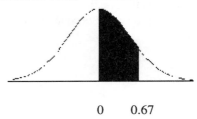

0    0.67

29.
The area is found by looking up $z = 1.57$ in Table E as shown in Block 1 of Procedure Table 6.  Area = 0.4418

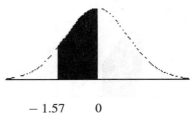

− 1.57    0

31.
The area is found by looking up $z = 2.83$ in Table E then subtracting the area from 0.5 as shown in Block 2 of Procedure Table 6.
$0.5 − 0.4977 = 0.0023$

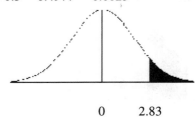

0    2.83

33.
The area is found by looking up z = 1.21 in Table E then subtracting the area from 0.5 as shown in Block 2 of Procedure Table 6.
$0.5 - 0.3869 = 0.1131$

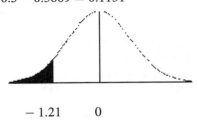

$-1.21 \qquad 0$

35.
The area is found by looking the values 2.46 and 1.74 in Table E and adding the areas together as shown in Block 4 of Procedure Table 6. $0.4931 + 0.4591 = 0.9522$

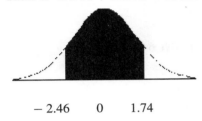

$-2.46 \qquad 0 \qquad 1.74$

37.
The area is found by looking up the values 1.46 and 2.97 in Table E and subtracting the areas as shown in Block 3 of Procedure Table 6. $0.4985 - 0.4279 = 0.0706$

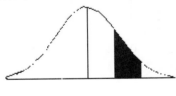

$0 \quad 1.46 \quad 2.97$

39.
The area is found by looking up z = 1.42 in Table E and adding 0.5 to it as shown in Block 5 of Procedure Table 6.
$0.5 + 0.4222 = 0.9222$

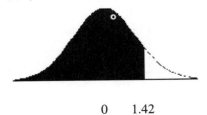

$0 \qquad 1.42$

41.
z = − 1.94, found by looking up the area 0.4738 in Table E to get 1.94; it is negative because the z value is on the left side of 0.

43.
z = − 2.13, found by subtracting 0.0166 from 0.5 to get 0.4834 then looking up the area to get z = 2.13; it is negative because the z value is on the left side of 0.

45.
z = − 1.26, found by subtracting 0.5 from 0.8962 to get 0.3962, then looking up the area in Table E to get z = 1.26; it is negative because the z value is on the left side of 0.

47.
a. z = − 2.28, found by subtracting 0.5 from 0.9886 to get 0.4886. Find the area in Table E, then find z. It is negative since the z value falls to the left of 0.

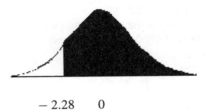

$-2.28 \qquad 0$

b. z = − 0.92, found by subtracting 0.5 from 0.8212 to get 0.3212. Find the area in Table E, then find z. It is negative since the z value falls to the left of 0.

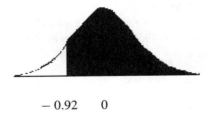

$-0.92 \qquad 0$

c. z = − 0.27, found by subtracting 0.5 from 0.6064 to get 0.1064. Find the area in Table E, then find z. It is negative since the z value falls to the left of 0.

47c. continued

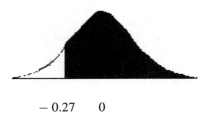

$$-0.27 \quad 0$$

49.
a. $z = \pm 1.96$, found by:
$0.05 \div 2 = 0.025$ is the area in each tail.
$0.5 - 0.025 = 0.4750$ is the area needed to determine z.

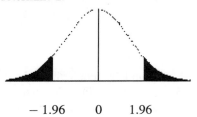

$$-1.96 \quad 0 \quad 1.96$$

b. $z = \pm 1.65$, found by:
$0.10 \div 2 = 0.05$ is the area in each tail.
$0.5 - 0.05 = 0.4500$ is the area needed to determine z.

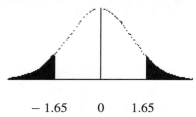

$$-1.65 \quad 0 \quad 1.65$$

c. $z = \pm 2.58$, found by:
$0.01 \div 2 = 0.005$ is the area in each tail.
$0.5 - 0.005 = 0.4950$ is the area needed to determine z.

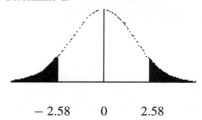

$$-2.58 \quad 0 \quad 2.58$$

51.
Using Table E:
$P(-1 < z < 1) = 2(0.3413) = 0.6826$
$P(-2 < z < 2) = 2(0.4772) = 0.9544$
$P(-3 < x < 3) = 2(0.4987) = 0.9974$
They are very close.

53.
For $z = -1.2$, area $= 0.3849$
$0.8671 - 0.3849 = 0.4822$
For area $= 0.4822$, $z = 2.10$
Thus, $P(-1.2 < z < 2.10) = 0.8671$

55.
For $z = -0.5$, area $= 0.1915$
$0.2345 - 0.1915 = 0.043$
For area $= 0.043$, $z = 0.11$
Thus, $P(-0.5 < z < 0.11) = 0.2345$

For $z = -0.5$, area $= 0.1915$
$0.2345 + 0.1915 = 0.4260$
For area $= 0.426$, $z = -1.45$
Thus, $P(-1.45 < z < -0.5) = 0.2345$

57.
$$y = \frac{e^{-\frac{(X-0)^2}{2(1)^2}}}{1\sqrt{2\pi}} = \frac{e^{\frac{-X^2}{2}}}{\sqrt{2\pi}}$$

EXERCISE SET 6-4

1.
$z = \frac{\$3.00 - \$5.39}{\$0.79} = -3.03$
area $= 0.4988$
$P(z < -3.03) = 0.5 - 0.4988 = 0.0012$ or $0.12\%$

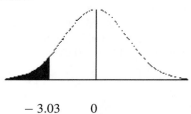

$$-3.03 \quad 0$$

3.
$z = \frac{X - \mu}{\sigma}$

a. $z = \frac{700,000 - 618,319}{50,200} = 1.63$
area $= 0.4484$

$P(z > 1.63) = 0.5 - 0.4484 = 0.0516$ or $5.16\%$

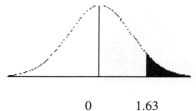

$$0 \quad 1.63$$

3. continued

b. $z = \frac{500,000 - 618,319}{50,200} = -2.36$
area = 0.4909

$z = \frac{600,000 - 618,319}{50,200} = -0.36$
area = 0.1406

$P(-2.36 < z < -0.36) = 0.4909 - 0.1406$
$P = 0.3503$ or 35.03%

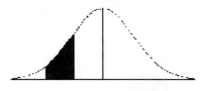

$-2.36 \quad -0.36$

5.
$z = \frac{X - \mu}{\sigma}$

a. $z = \frac{200 - 225}{10} = -2.5$
area = 0.4938

$z = \frac{220 - 225}{10} = -0.5$
area = 0.1915

$P(-2.5 < z < -0.5) =$
$0.4938 - 0.1915 = 0.3023$ or 30.23%

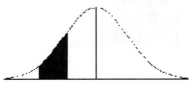

$-2.5 \quad -0.5$

b. $z = -2.5$
area = 0.4938

$P(z < -2.5) = 0.5 - 0.4938 = 0.0062$ or
0.62%

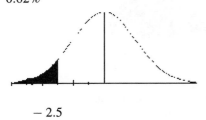

$-2.5$

7.
$z = \frac{X - \mu}{\sigma}$

a. $z = \frac{\$90,000 - \$85,900}{\$11,000} = 0.37$
area = 0.1443

$P(z > 0.37) = 0.5 - 0.1443 = 0.3557$
or 35.57%

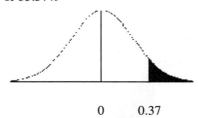

$0 \qquad 0.37$

b. $z = \frac{\$75,000 - \$85,900}{\$11,000} = -0.99$
area = 0.3389

$P(z > -0.99) = 0.5 + 0.3389$
$= 0.8389$ or 83.89%

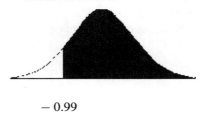

$-0.99$

9.
$z = \frac{X - \mu}{\sigma}$

a. $z = \frac{1.5 - 3.2}{0.56} = -3.04 \quad$ area = 0.4988

$P(z < -3.04) = 0.5 - 0.4988 = 0.0012$

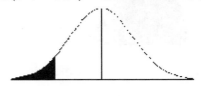

$-3.04 \qquad 0$

b. $z = \frac{2 - 3.2}{0.56} = -2.14 \qquad$ area = 0.4838

$z = \frac{3 - 3.2}{0.56} = -0.36 \qquad$ area = 0.1406

$P(-2.14 < z < -0.36) =$
$0.4838 - 0.1406 = 0.3432$

9b. continued

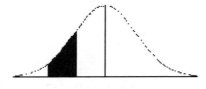

$-2.14 \quad -0.36$

c. $z = \frac{3.2-3.2}{0.56} = 0$      area $= 0.5$

$P(z > 0) = 0.5$

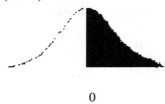

$0$

d. For an 18 month (1.5 year) warranty,
$z = -3.04$.
$P(z < -3.04) = .5 - 0.4988 = 0.0012$
Hence, 0.12% of the ovens would be
replaced.

11.
$z \geq \frac{X-\mu}{\sigma}$

a. $z = \frac{1000-3262}{1100} = -2.06$
area $= 0.4803$

$P(z \geq -2.06) = 0.5 + 0.4803 = 0.9803$
or 98.03%

$-2.06$

b. $z = \frac{4000-3262}{1100} = 0.67$
area $= 0.2486$

$P(z > 0.67) = 0.5 - 0.2486 = 0.2514$ or
25.14%

11b. continued

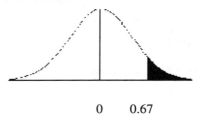

$0 \quad\quad 0.67$

c. $z = \frac{3000-3262}{1100} = -0.24$
area $= 0.0948$

$P(-0.24 < z < 0.67) =$
$0.0948 + 0.2486 = 0.3434$ or 34.34%

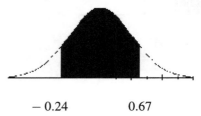

$-0.24 \quad\quad\quad 0.67$

13.
a. $z = \frac{350-380}{16} = -1.88$
area $= 0.4699$

$P(z \geq -1.88) = 0.5 + 0.4699 = 0.9699$

$-1.88 \quad\quad 0$

b. $z = \frac{395-380}{16} = 0.94$
area $= 0.3264$

$P(z \leq 0.94) = 0.5 + 0.3264 = 0.8264$

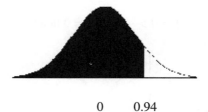

$0 \quad\quad 0.94$

c. Use the range rule of thumb:
If $\frac{\text{Range}}{4} = 16$, then the range is about
$16 \cdot 4 = 64$.

15.
a.  $z = \frac{15-23.5}{3.6} = -2.36$     area $= 0.4909$

$z = \frac{22-23.5}{3.6} = -0.42$     area $= 0.1628$

P($-2.36 < z < -0.42$) =
$0.4909 - 0.1628 = 0.3281$

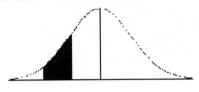

$-2.36$   $-0.42$

b.  $z = \frac{18-23.5}{3.6} = -1.53$     area $= 0.4370$

$z = \frac{25-23.5}{3.6} = 0.42$     area $= 0.1628$

P(z $< -1.53$ or z $> 0.42$) =
$(0.5 - 0.4370) + (0.5 - 0.1628) =$
$0.063 + 0.3372 = 0.4002$

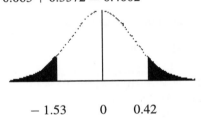

$-1.53$     0     0.42

c. For 15 minutes, z $= -2.36$.
P(z $< -2.36$) $= 0.5 - 0.4909 = 0.0091$
Since the probability is small, it is not likely
that a person would be seated in less than 15
minutes.

17.
The middle 66% means that 33% of the area
will be on either side of the mean. Thus,
area $= 0.33$ and z $= \pm 0.95$.
$x = -0.95(1025) + 6492 = \$5518.25$
$x = 0.95(1025) + 6492 = \$7465.75$

The prices are between $5518.25 and
$7465.75.

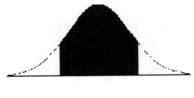

$5518.25         $7465.75

17. continued
Yes, a boat priced at $5550 would be sold in
this store.

19.
The middle 80% means that 40% of the area
will be on either side of the mean. The
corresponding z scores will be $\pm 1.28$.
$x = -1.28(92) + 1810 = 1692.24$ sq. ft.
$x = 1.28(92) + 1810 = 1927.76$ sq. ft.

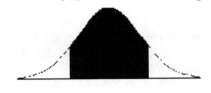

1692      1810      1928

21.
$z = \frac{1200-949}{100} = 2.51$
area $= 0.4940$

P( z $> 2.51$) $= 0.5 - 0.4940 = 0.006$ or
0.6%

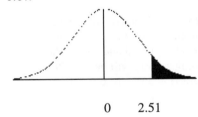

0      2.51

For the least expensive 10%, the area is 0.4
on the left side of the curve. Thus,
z $= -1.28$.
$x = -1.28(100) + 949 = \$821$

23.
The middle 60% means that 30% of the area
will be on either side of the mean. The
corresponding z scores will be $\pm 0.84$.
$x = -0.84(1150) + 8256 = \$7290$
$x = 0.84(1150) + 8256 = \$9222$

$7290   $8256   $9222

**25.**

For the fewest 15%, the area is 0.35 on the left side of the curve. Thus, $z = -1.04$.
$x = -1.04(1.7) + 5.9$
$x = 4.132$ days

For the longest 25%, the area is 0.25 on the right side of the curve. Thus, $z = 0.67$.
$x = 0.67(1.7) + 5.9$
$x = 7.039$ days or 7.04 days

**27.**

The bottom 18% means that 32% of the area is between 0 and $-z$. The corresponding z score will be $-0.92$.
$x = -0.92(6256) + 24{,}596 = \$18{,}840.48$

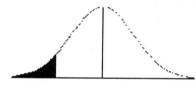

$\$18{,}840.48 \qquad \$24{,}596$

**29.**

The 10% to be exchanged would be at the left, or bottom, of the curve; therefore, 40% of the area is between 0 and $-z$. The corresponding z score will be $-1.28$.
$x = -1.28(5) + 25 = 18.6$ months.

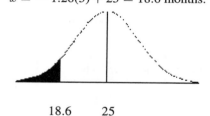

$18.6 \qquad 25$

**31.**

a. $\mu = 120 \qquad \sigma = 20$
b. $\mu = 15 \qquad \sigma = 2.5$
c. $\mu = 30 \qquad \sigma = 5$

**33.**

There are several mathematical tests that can be used including drawing a histogram and calculating Pearson's index of skewness.

**35.**

2.87% area in the right tail of the curve means that 47.13% of the area is between 0 and z, corresponding to a z score of 1.90.

**35. continued**
$z = \frac{X - \mu}{\sigma}$
$1.90 = \frac{112 - 110}{\sigma}$
$1.90\sigma = 2$
$\sigma = 1.05$

**37.**

1.25% of the area in each tail means that 48.75% of the area is between 0 and $\pm z$. The corresponding z scores are $\pm 2.24$.
Then $\mu = \frac{42 + 48}{2} = 45$ and $X = \mu + z\sigma$.
$48 = 45 + 2.24\sigma$
$\sigma = 1.34$

**39.**
Histogram:

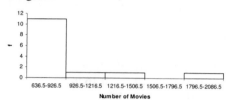

The histogram shows a positive skew.

$PI = \frac{3(970.2 - 853.5)}{376.5} = 0.93$

$IQR = Q_3 - Q_1 = 910 - 815 = 95$
$1.5(IQR) = 1.5(95) = 142.5$
$Q_1 - 142.5 = 672.5$
$Q_3 + 142.5 = 1052.5$
There are several outliers.
Conclusion: The distribution is not normal.

**41.**
Histogram:

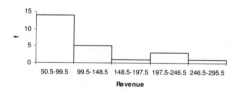

The histogram shows a positive skew.

$PI = \frac{3(115.3 - 92.5)}{66.32} = 1.03$

$IQR = Q_3 - Q_1 = 154.5 - 67 = 87.5$
$1.5(IQR) = 1.5(87.5) = 131.25$
$Q_1 - 131.25 = -64.25$
$Q_3 + 131.25 = 285.75$
There is one outlier.
Conclusion: The distribution is not normal.

EXERCISE SET 6-5

1.
The distribution is called the sampling distribution of sample means.

3.
The mean of the sample means is equal to the population mean.

5.
The distribution will be approximately normal when sample size is large.

7.
$$z = \frac{\overline{X} - \mu}{\sigma / \sqrt{n}}$$

9.
$$z = \frac{\overline{X} - \mu}{\frac{\sigma}{\sqrt{n}}} = \frac{\$175 - \$186.80}{\frac{\$32}{\sqrt{50}}} = -2.61$$
area = 0.4955
$P(z < -2.61) = 0.5 - 0.4955 = 0.0045$ or 0.45%

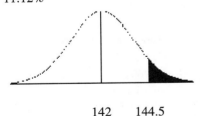

$175 \qquad \$186.8$

11.
$$z = \frac{\overline{X} - \mu}{\frac{\sigma}{\sqrt{n}}} = \frac{144.5 - 142}{\frac{12.3}{\sqrt{36}}} = 1.22$$
area = 0.3888
$P(z > 1.22) = 0.5 - 0.3888 = 0.1112$ or 11.12%

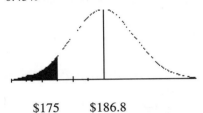

142 \qquad 144.5

13.
$$z = \frac{\overline{X} - \mu}{\frac{\sigma}{\sqrt{n}}} = \frac{\$2.00 - \$2.02}{\frac{\$0.08}{\sqrt{40}}} = -1.58$$
area = 0.4429
$P(z < -1.58) = 0.5 - 0.4429 = 0.0571$ or 5.71%

13. continued

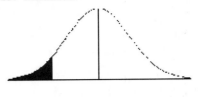

$2.00 \qquad \$2.02$

15.
a. $z = \frac{\overline{X} - \mu}{\sigma} = \frac{670 - 660}{35} = 0.29$
area = 0.1141
$P(z > 0.29) = 0.5 - 0.1141 = 0.3859$

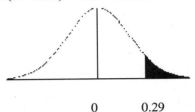

0 \qquad 0.29

b. $z = \frac{\overline{X} - \mu}{\frac{\sigma}{\sqrt{n}}} = \frac{670 - 660}{\frac{35}{\sqrt{10}}} = 0.90$
area = 0.3159
$P(z > 0.90) = 0.5 - 0.3159 = 0.1841$

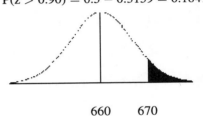

660 \qquad 670

c. Individual values are more variable than means.

17.
$$z = \frac{\overline{X} - \mu}{\frac{\sigma}{\sqrt{n}}} = \frac{120 - 123}{\frac{21}{\sqrt{15}}} = -0.55$$
area = 0.2088
$$z = \frac{\overline{X} - \mu}{\frac{\sigma}{\sqrt{n}}} = \frac{126 - 123}{\frac{21}{\sqrt{15}}} = 0.55$$
area = 0.2088
$P(-0.55 < z < 0.55) = 2(0.2088) = 0.4176$ or 41.76%

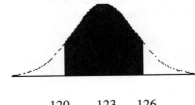

120 \qquad 123 \qquad 126

19.
$$z = \frac{\overline{X}-\mu}{\frac{\sigma}{\sqrt{n}}} = \frac{1980-2000}{\frac{187.5}{\sqrt{50}}} = -0.75$$
area = 0.2734
$$z = \frac{\overline{X}-\mu}{\frac{\sigma}{\sqrt{n}}} = \frac{1990-2000}{\frac{187.5}{\sqrt{50}}} = -0.38$$
area = 0.1480
$P(-0.75 < z < -0.38) = 0.2734 - 0.1480 = 0.1254$ or 12.54%

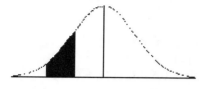

1980  1990  2000

21.
a. $z = \frac{X-\mu}{\sigma} = \frac{43-46.2}{8} = -0.4$
area = 0.1554
$P(z < -0.4) = 0.5 - 0.1554 = 0.3446$ or 34.46%

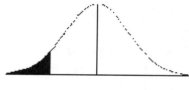

43          46.2

b. $z = \frac{43-46.2}{\frac{8}{\sqrt{50}}} = -2.83$     area = 0.4977
$P(z < -2.83) = 0.5 - 0.4977 = 0.0023$ or 0.23%

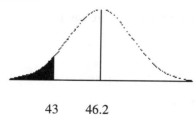

43          46.2

c. Yes, since it is within one standard deviation of the mean.

d. Very unlikely, since the probability would be less than 1%.

23.
a. $z = \frac{220-215}{15} = 0.33$       area = 0.1293
$P(z > 0.33) = 0.5 - 0.1293 = 0.3707$ or 37.07%

23a. continued

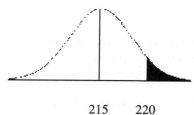

215        220

b. $z = \frac{220-215}{\frac{15}{\sqrt{25}}} = 1.67$       area = 0.4525
$P(z > 1.67) = 0.5 - 0.4525 = 0.0475$ or 4.75%

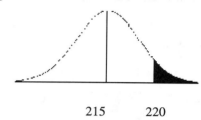

215                220

25.
$$z = \frac{100-106}{\frac{16.1}{\sqrt{35}}} = -2.20$$   area = 0.4861

$$z = \frac{110-106}{\frac{16.1}{\sqrt{35}}} = 1.47$$     area = 0.4292

$P(-2.20 < z < 1.47) = 0.4861 + 0.4292$
$= 0.9153$ or 91.53%

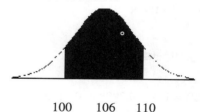

100      106      110

27.
Since 50 > 0.05(800) or 40, the correction factor is necessary.
It is $\sqrt{\frac{800-50}{800-1}} = 0.969$
$$z = \frac{\overline{X}-\mu}{\frac{\sigma}{\sqrt{n}} \cdot \sqrt{\frac{N-n}{n-1}}} = \frac{83,500-82,000}{\frac{5000}{\sqrt{50}}(0.969)} = 2.19$$
area = 0.4857
$P(z > 2.19) = 0.5 - 0.4857 = 0.0143$ or 1.43%

# Chapter 6 - The Normal Distribution

**27. continued**

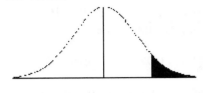

82,000  83,500

**29.**

$$\sigma_x = \frac{\sigma}{\sqrt{n}} = \frac{15}{\sqrt{100}} = 1.5$$

$$2(1.5) = \frac{15}{\sqrt{n}}$$

$$3 \cdot \sqrt{n} = 15$$

$$\sqrt{n} = 5$$

n = 25, the sample size necessary to double the standard error.

**EXERCISE SET 6-6**

**1.**
When p is approximately 0.5 and as n increases, the shape of the binomial distribution becomes similar to the normal distribution. The normal approximation should be used only when $n \cdot p$ and $n \cdot q$ are both greater than or equal to 5. The correction for continuity is necessary because the normal distribution is continuous and the binomial is discrete.

**2.**
For each problem use the following formulas:
$$\mu = np \quad \sigma = \sqrt{npq} \quad z = \frac{X-\mu}{\sigma}$$
Be sure to correct each X for continuity.
a. $\mu = 0.5(30) = 15$
$\sigma = \sqrt{(0.5)(0.5)(30)} = 2.74$

$z = \frac{17.5-15}{2.74} = 0.91$ area = 0.3186

$z = \frac{18.5-15}{2.74} = 1.28$ area = 0.3997

$P(17.5 < X < 18.5) = 0.3997 - 0.3186$
$= 0.0811 = 8.11\%$

**2a. continued**

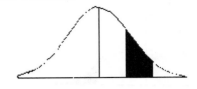

15  17.5  18.5

b. $\mu = 0.8(50) = 40$
$\sigma = \sqrt{(50)(0.8)(0.2)} = 2.83$

$z = \frac{43.5-40}{2.83} = 1.24$ area = 0.3925

$z = \frac{44.5-40}{2.83} = 1.59$ area = 0.4441

$P(43.5 < X < 44.5) = 0.4441 - 0.3925$
$= 0.0516$ or 5.16%

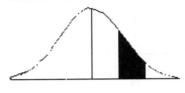

40  43.5  44.5

c. $\mu = 0.1(100) = 10$
$\sigma = \sqrt{(0.1)(0.9)(100)} = 3$

$z = \frac{11.5-10}{3} = 0.50$ area = 0.1915

$z = \frac{12.5-10}{3} = 0.83$ area = 0.2967

$P(11.5 < X < 12.5) = 0.2967 - 0.1915$
$= 0.1052$ or 10.52%

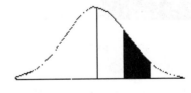

10  11.5  12.5

d. $\mu = 10(0.5) = 5$
$\sigma = \sqrt{(0.5)(0.5)(10)} = 1.58$

$z = \frac{6.5-5}{1.58} = 0.95$ area = 0.3289

$P(X \geq 6.5) = 0.5 - 0.3289 = 0.1711$ or 17.11%

57

2d. continued

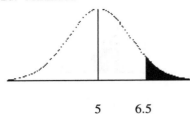

5          6.5

e. $\mu = 20(0.7) = 14$
$\sigma = \sqrt{(20)(0.7)(0.3)} = 2.05$

$z = \frac{12.5 - 14}{2.05} = -0.73$          area = 0.2673

$P(X \leq 12.5) = 0.5 - 0.2673 = 0.2327$ or 23.27%

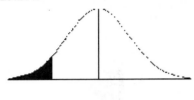

12.5          14

f. $\mu = 50(0.6) = 30$
$\sigma = \sqrt{(50)(0.6)(0.4)} = 3.46$

$z = \frac{40.5 - 30}{3.46} = 3.03$          area = 0.4988

$P(X \leq 40.5) = 0.5 + 0.4988 = 0.9988$ or 99.88%

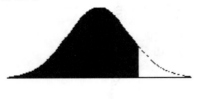

30          40.5

3.
a. $np = 20(0.50) = 10 \geq 5$          Yes
   $nq = 20(0.50) = 10 \geq 5$
b. $np = 10(0.60) = 6 \geq 5$          No
   $nq = 10(0.40) = 4 < 5$
c. $np = 40(0.90) = 36 \geq 5$          No
   $nq = 40(0.10) = 4 < 5$
d. $np = 50(0.20) = 10 \geq 5$          Yes
   $nq = 50(0.80) = 40 \geq 5$
e. $np = 30(0.80) = 24 \geq 5$          Yes
   $nq = 30(0.20) = 6 \geq 5$
f. $np = 20(0.85) = 17 \geq 5$          No
   $nq = 20(0.15) = 3 > 5$

5.
$p = \frac{2}{5} = 0.4$          $\mu = 400(0.4) = 160$
$\sigma = \sqrt{(400)(0.4)(0.6)} = 9.8$

$z = \frac{169.5 - 160}{9.8} = 0.97$          area = 0.3340

$P(X > 169.5) = 0.5 - 0.3340 = 0.1660$ or 16.6%

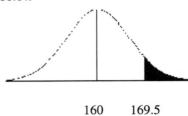

160          169.5

7.
$\mu = 300(0.509) = 152.7$
$\sigma = \sqrt{(300)(0.509)(0.491)} = 8.66$

$z = \frac{175.5 - 152.7}{8.66} = 2.63$ area = 0.4957

$P(X > 175.5) = 0.5 - 0.4957 = 0.0043$

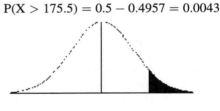

152.7          175.5

9.
$\mu = 180(0.236) = 42.48$
$\sigma = \sqrt{(180)(0.236)(0.764)} = 5.70$

$z = \frac{50.5 - 42.48}{5.70} = 1.41$          area = 0.4207

$P(X > 50.5) = 0.5 - 0.4207 = 0.0793$

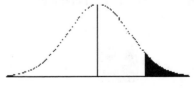

42.48          50.5

11.
$\mu = 300(0.167) = 50.1$
$\sigma = \sqrt{(300)(0.167)(0.833)} = 6.46$

$z = \frac{50.5 - 50.1}{6.46} = 0.06$          area = 0.0239

11. continued
$P(X > 50.5) = 0.5 - 0.0239 = 0.4761$

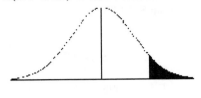

50.1    50.5

13.
$\mu = 350(0.35) = 122.5$
$\sigma = \sqrt{(350)(0.35)(0.65)} = 8.92$

$z = \frac{99.5 - 122.5}{8.92} = -2.58$

$P(X > 99.5) = 0.5 + 0.4951 = 0.9951$ or
99.51%  Yes.

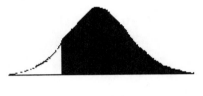

99.5    122.5

REVIEW EXERCISES - CHAPTER 6

1.
a.  0.4744

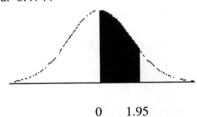

0       1.95

b.  0.1443

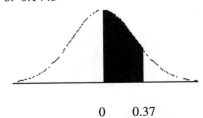

0       0.37

c.  $0.4656 - 0.4066 = 0.0590$

1c.  continued

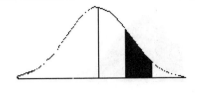

0    1.32  1.82

d.  $0.3531 + 0.4798 = 0.8329$

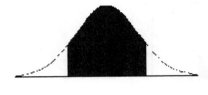

$-1.05$      0      2.05

e.  $0.2019 + 0.0120 = 0.2139$

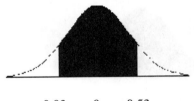

$-0.03$     0      0.53

f.  $0.3643 + 0.4641 = 0.8284$

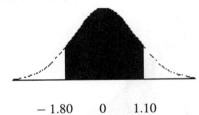

$-1.80$     0      1.10

g.  $0.5 - 0.4767 = 0.0233$

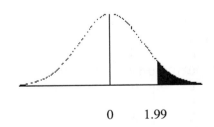

0      1.99

h.  $0.5 + 0.4131 = 0.9131$

**1h. continued**

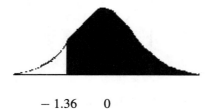

$$-1.36 \qquad 0$$

i. $0.5 - 0.4817 = 0.0183$

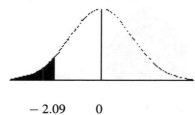

$$-2.09 \qquad 0$$

j. $0.5 + 0.4535 = 0.9535$

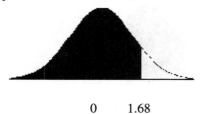

$$0 \qquad 1.68$$

**3.**

a. $z = \frac{27,635 - 27,635}{2550} = 0 \qquad$ area $= 0.5$

$P(z > 0) = 0.5$

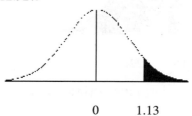

$$0$$

b. $z = \frac{25,000 - 27,635}{2550} = -1.03$
area $= 0.3485$

$P(z < -1.03) = 0.5 - 0.3485 = 0.1515$

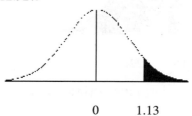

$$-1.03 \qquad 0$$

**3. continued**
c. About 85% of auto mechanics would be earning more than $25,000.

**5.**
a. $z = \frac{65 - 63}{8} = 0.25 \qquad$ area $= 0.0987$

$P(z > 0.25) = 0.5 - 0.0987 = 0.4013$ or 40.13%

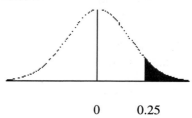

$$0 \qquad 0.25$$

b. $z = \frac{72 - 63}{8} = 1.13 \qquad$ area $= 0.3708$

$P(z > 1.13) = 0.5 - 0.3708 = 0.1292$ or 12.92%

$$0 \qquad 1.13$$

**7.**
a. $z = \frac{18 - 19.32}{2.44} = -0.54 \qquad$ area $= 0.2054$

$P(z > -0.54) = 0.5 + 0.2054 = 0.7054$

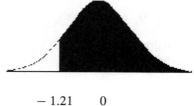

$$-0.54 \qquad 0$$

b. $z = \frac{18 - 19.32}{\frac{2.44}{\sqrt{5}}} = -1.21 \qquad$ area $= 0.3869$

$P(z > -1.21) = 0.5 + 0.3869 = 0.8869$

$$-1.21 \qquad 0$$

**9.**
The middle 40% means that 20% of the area is on either side of the mean. The corresponding z scores are $\pm 0.52$.
$X_1 = 100 + (0.52)(15) = 107.8$
$X_2 = 100 + (-0.52)(15) = 92.2$
The scores should be between 92.2 and 107.8.

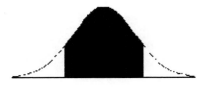

92.2    100    107.8

**11.**
$z = \frac{3.4-3.7}{\frac{0.6}{\sqrt{32}}} = -2.83$          area $= 0.4977$

$P(\overline{X} < 3.4) = 0.5 - 0.4977 = 0.0023$ or 0.23%

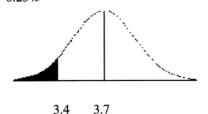

3.4        3.7

Yes, since the probability is less than 1%.

**13.**
$\mu = 200(0.18) = 36$
$\sigma = \sqrt{(200)(0.18)(0.82)} = 5.43$

$z = \frac{40.5-36}{5.43} = 0.83$          area $= 0.2967$

$P(X > 40.5) = 0.5 - 0.2967 = 0.2033$ or 20.33%

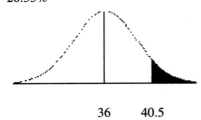

36        40.5

**15.**
$\mu = 200(0.2) = 40$
$\sigma = \sqrt{(200)(0.2)(0.8)} = 5.66$

$z = \frac{49.5-40}{5.66} = 1.68$          area $= 0.4535$

**15. continued**
$P(X \geq 49.5) = 0.5 - 0.4535 = 0.0465$ or 4.65%

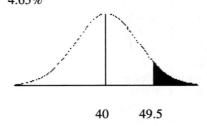

40        49.5

**17.**
Histogram:

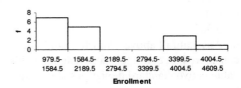

The histogram shows a positive skew.

$PI = \frac{3(2136.1-1755)}{1171.7} = 0.98$

$IQR = Q_3 - Q_1$
$IQR = 2827 - 1320 = 1507$
$1.5(IQR) = 1.5(1507) = 2260.5$
$Q_1 - 2260.5 = -940.5$
$Q_3 + 2260.5 = 5087.5$

There are no outliers.
Conclusion: The distribution is not normal.

**CHAPTER 6 QUIZ**

1. False, the total area is equal to one.
2. True
3. True
4. True
5. False, the area is positive.
6. False, it applies to means taken from the same population.
7. a
8. a
9. b
10. b
11. c
12. 0.5
13. Sampling error
14. The population mean
15. Standard error of the mean
16. 5

17. 5%

18. the areas are:

a. 0.4332    f. 0.8284

b. 0.3944    g. 0.0401

c. 0.0344    h. 0..8997

d. 0.1029    i. 0.017

e. 0.2912    j. 0.9131

19. the probabilities are:

a. 0.4846    f. 0.0384

b. 0.4693    g. 0.0089

c. 0.9334    h. 0.9582

d. 0.0188    i. 0.9788

e. 0.7461    j. 0.8461

20. the probabilities are:

a. 0.7734

b. 0.0516

c. 0.3837

d. Any rainfall above 65 inches could be considered an extremely wet year since this value is two standard deviations above the mean.

21. the probabilities are:

a. 0.0668    c. 0.4649

b. 0.0228    d. 0.0934

22. the probabilities are:

a. 0.4525    c. 0.3707

b. 0.3707    d. 0.019

23. the probabilities are:

a. 0.0013    c. 0.0081

b. 0.5      d. 0.5511

24. the probabilities are:

a. 0.0037    c. 0.5

b. 0.0228    d. 0.3232

25. 8.804 cm

26. The lowest acceptable score is 121.24.

27. 0.015

28. 0.9738

29. 0.0495; no

30. 0.0630

31. 0.8577

32. 0.0495

33. The distribution is not normal.

34. The distribution is approximately normal.

Note: Answers may vary due to rounding.

EXERCISE SET 7-2

**1.**
A point estimate of a parameter specifies a specific value such as $\mu = 87$, whereas an interval estimate specifies a range of values for the parameter such as $84 < \mu < 90$. The advantage of an interval estimate is that a specific confidence level (say 95%) can be selected, and one can be 95% confident that the parameter being estimated lies in the interval.

**3.**
The maximum error of estimate is the likely range of values to the right or left of the statistic which may contain the parameter.

**5.**
A good estimator should be unbiased, consistent, and relatively efficient.

**7.**
To determine sample size, the maximum error of estimate and the degree of confidence must be specified and the population standard deviation must be known.

**9.**
a. 2.58     d. 1.65
b. 2.33     e. 1.88
c. 1.96

**11.**
a. $\overline{X} = 82$ is the point estimate for $\mu$.

b. $\overline{X} - z_{\frac{\alpha}{2}}\left(\frac{s}{\sqrt{n}}\right) < \mu < \overline{X} + z_{\frac{\alpha}{2}}\left(\frac{s}{\sqrt{n}}\right)$
$82 - (1.96)\left(\frac{15}{\sqrt{35}}\right) < \mu < 82 + (1.96)\left(\frac{15}{\sqrt{35}}\right)$
$82 - 4.97 < \mu < 82 + 4.97$
$77 < \mu < 87$

c. $82 - (2.58)\left(\frac{15}{\sqrt{35}}\right) < \mu < 82 + (2.58)\left(\frac{15}{\sqrt{35}}\right)$
$82 - 6.54 < \mu < 82 + 6.54$
$75 < \mu < 89$

d. The 99% confidence interval is larger because the confidence level is larger.

**13.**
a. $\overline{X} = 12.6$ is the point estimate for $\mu$.

**13. continued**
b. $\overline{X} - z_{\frac{\alpha}{2}}\left(\frac{\sigma}{\sqrt{n}}\right) < \mu < \overline{X} + z_{\frac{\alpha}{2}}\left(\frac{\sigma}{\sqrt{n}}\right)$
$12.6 - 1.65\left(\frac{2.5}{\sqrt{40}}\right) < \mu < 12.6 + 1.65\left(\frac{2.5}{\sqrt{40}}\right)$
$12.6 - 0.652 < \mu < 12.6 + 0.652$
$11.9 < \mu < 13.3$

c. It would be highly unlikely since this is far larger than 13.3 minutes.

**15.**
$\overline{X} - z_{\frac{\alpha}{2}}\left(\frac{s}{\sqrt{n}}\right) < \mu < \overline{X} + z_{\frac{\alpha}{2}}\left(\frac{s}{\sqrt{n}}\right)$
$\$150,000 - 1.96\left(\frac{15,000}{\sqrt{35}}\right) < \mu <$
$\$150,000 + 1.96\left(\frac{15,000}{\sqrt{35}}\right)$
$\$150,000 - 4969.51 < \mu <$
$\$150,000 + 4969.51$

$\$145,030 < \mu < \$154,970$

**17.**
$\overline{X} = 5000 \quad s = 900$
$5000 - 1.96\left(\frac{900}{\sqrt{415}}\right) < \mu < 5000 +$
$\quad 1.96\left(\frac{900}{\sqrt{415}}\right)$
$4913 < \mu < 5087$

4000 hours does not seem reasonable since it is outside this interval.

**19.**
$\overline{X} - z_{\frac{\alpha}{2}}\left(\frac{s}{\sqrt{n}}\right) < \mu < \overline{X} + z_{\frac{\alpha}{2}}\left(\frac{s}{\sqrt{n}}\right)$
$61.2 - 1.96\left(\frac{7.9}{\sqrt{84}}\right) < \mu < 61.2 + 1.96\left(\frac{7.9}{\sqrt{84}}\right)$
$61.2 - 1.69 < \mu < 61.2 + 1.69$
$59.5 < \mu < 62.9$

**21.**
$n = \left[\frac{z_{\frac{\alpha}{2}}\,\sigma}{E}\right]^2 = \left[\frac{(2.58)(6.2)}{1.5}\right]^2$
$= (10.664)^2 = 113.7$ or 114

**23.**
$n = \left[\frac{z_{\frac{\alpha}{2}}\,\sigma}{E}\right]^2 = \left[\frac{(1.96)(2.5)}{1}\right]^2$

$= (4.9)^2 = 24.01$ or 25

**25.**
$n = \left[\frac{z_{\frac{\alpha}{2}}\,\sigma}{E}\right]^2 = \left[\frac{(1.65)(1100)}{150}\right]^2$

$= (12.1)^2 = 146.4$ or 147

EXERCISE SET 7-3

**1.**
The characteristics of the t-distribution are: It is bell-shaped, symmetrical about the mean, and never touches the x-axis. The mean, median, and mode are equal to 0 and are located at the center of the distribution. The variance is greater than 1. The t-distribution is a family of curves based on degrees of freedom. As sample size increases the t-distribution approaches the normal distribution.

**3.**
The t-distribution should be used when $\sigma$ is unknown and n < 30.

**4.**
a. 2.898 where d. f. = 17
b. 2.074 where d. f. = 22
c. 2.624 where d. f. = 14
d. 1.833 where d. f. = 9
e. 2.093 where d. f. = 19

**5.**
$\overline{X} - t_{\frac{\alpha}{2}}(\frac{s}{\sqrt{n}}) < \mu < \overline{X} + t_{\frac{\alpha}{2}}(\frac{s}{\sqrt{n}})$
$16 - (2.861)(\frac{2}{\sqrt{20}}) < \mu < 16 + (2.861)(\frac{2}{\sqrt{20}})$
$16 - 1.28 < \mu < 16 + 1.28$
$15 < \mu < 17$

**7.**
$\overline{X} = 33.4 \quad s = 28.7$
$\overline{X} - t_{\frac{\alpha}{2}}(\frac{s}{\sqrt{n}}) < \mu < \overline{X} + t_{\frac{\alpha}{2}}(\frac{s}{\sqrt{n}})$
$33.4 - 1.746(\frac{28.7}{\sqrt{17}}) < \mu < 33.4 + 1.746(\frac{28.7}{\sqrt{17}})$
$33.4 - 12.2 < \mu < 33.4 + 12.2$
$21.2 < \mu < 45.6$

The point estimate is 33.4 and is close to the actual population mean of 32, which is within the 90% confidence interval. The mean may not be the best estimate since the data value 132 is large and possibly an outlier.

**9.**
$\overline{X} - t_{\frac{\alpha}{2}}(\frac{s}{\sqrt{n}}) < \mu < \overline{X} + t_{\frac{\alpha}{2}}(\frac{s}{\sqrt{n}})$
$276 - 2.015(\frac{12}{\sqrt{6}}) < \mu <$
$\quad 276 + 2.015(\frac{12}{\sqrt{6}})$
$276 - 9.9 < \mu < 276 + 9.9$
$266.1 < \mu < 285.9$ or $266 < \mu < 286$
The coach's claim is highly unlikely.

**11.**
$\overline{X} - t_{\frac{\alpha}{2}}(\frac{s}{\sqrt{n}}) < \mu < \overline{X} + t_{\frac{\alpha}{2}}(\frac{s}{\sqrt{n}})$
$14.3 - 2.052(\frac{2}{\sqrt{28}}) < \mu < 14.3 + 2.052(\frac{2}{\sqrt{28}})$
$14.3 - 0.8 < \mu < 14.3 + 0.8$
$13.5 < \mu < 15.1$
The employees should allow about 30 minutes.

**13.**
$\overline{X} - t_{\frac{\alpha}{2}}(\frac{s}{\sqrt{n}}) < \mu < \overline{X} + t_{\frac{\alpha}{2}}(\frac{s}{\sqrt{n}})$
$18.53 - 2.064(\frac{3}{\sqrt{25}}) < \mu <$
$\quad 18.53 + 2.064(\frac{3}{\sqrt{25}})$
$18.53 - 1.238 < \mu < 18.53 + 1.238$
$\$17.29 < \mu < \$19.77$

**15.**
$\overline{X} - t_{\frac{\alpha}{2}}(\frac{s}{\sqrt{n}}) < \mu < \overline{X} + t_{\frac{\alpha}{2}}(\frac{s}{\sqrt{n}})$
$115 - 2.571(\frac{6}{\sqrt{6}}) < \mu < 115 + 2.571(\frac{6}{\sqrt{6}})$
$115 - 6.298 < \mu < 115 + 6.298$
$109 < \mu < 121$

**17.**
$\overline{X} = 41.6 \quad x = 5.995$
$\overline{X} - t_{\frac{\alpha}{2}}(\frac{s}{\sqrt{n}}) < \mu < \overline{X} + t_{\frac{\alpha}{2}}(\frac{s}{\sqrt{n}})$
$41.6 - 2.093(\frac{5.995}{\sqrt{20}}) < \mu <$
$\quad 41.6 + 2.093(\frac{5.995}{\sqrt{20}})$
$41.6 - 2.806 < \mu < 41.6 + 2.806$
$38.8 < \mu < 44.4$

**19.**
$\overline{X} - t_{\frac{\alpha}{2}}(\frac{s}{\sqrt{n}}) < \mu < \overline{X} + t_{\frac{\alpha}{2}}(\frac{s}{\sqrt{n}})$
$\$56,718 - 2.052(\frac{650}{\sqrt{28}}) < \mu <$
$\quad \$56,718 + 2.052(\frac{650}{\sqrt{28}})$
$\$56,466 < \mu < \$56,970$
He should use $\$56,466$.

**21.**
$\overline{X} = 2.175 \quad s = 0.585$
For $\mu > \overline{X} - t_{\frac{\alpha}{2}}(\frac{s}{\sqrt{n}})$:
$\mu > 2.175 - 1.729(\frac{0.585}{\sqrt{20}})$
$\mu > 2.175 - 0.226$
Thus, $\mu > \$1.95$ means that one can be 95% confident that the mean revenue is greater than $\$1.95$.

**21. continued**

For $\mu < \overline{X} + t_{\frac{\alpha}{2}}(\frac{s}{\sqrt{n}})$:

$\mu < 2.175 + 1.729(\frac{0.585}{\sqrt{20}})$

$\mu < 2.175 + 0.226$

Thus, $\mu < \$2.40$ means that one can be 95% confident that the mean revenue is less than $2.40.

**EXERCISE SET 7-4**

**1.**

a. $\hat{p} = \frac{40}{80} = 0.5$ $\qquad$ $\hat{q} = \frac{40}{80} = 0.5$

b. $\hat{p} = \frac{90}{200} = 0.45$ $\qquad$ $\hat{q} = \frac{110}{200} = 0.55$

c. $\hat{p} = \frac{60}{130} = 0.46$ $\qquad$ $\hat{q} = \frac{70}{130} = 0.54$

d. $\hat{p} = \frac{35}{60} = 0.58$ $\qquad$ $\hat{q} = \frac{25}{60} = 0.42$

e. $\hat{p} = \frac{43}{95} = 0.45$ $\qquad$ $\hat{q} = \frac{52}{95} = 0.55$

**2.**

For each part, change the percent to a decimal by dividing by 100, and find $\hat{q}$ using $\hat{q} = 1 - \hat{p}$.

a. $\hat{p} = 0.15$ $\qquad$ $\hat{q} = 1 - 0.15 = 0.85$
b. $\hat{p} = 0.37$ $\qquad$ $\hat{q} = 1 - 0.37 = 0.63$
c. $\hat{p} = 0.71$ $\qquad$ $\hat{q} = 1 - 0.71 = 0.29$
d. $\hat{p} = 0.51$ $\qquad$ $\hat{q} = 1 - 0.51 = 0.49$
e. $\hat{p} = 0.79$ $\qquad$ $\hat{q} = 1 - 0.79 = 0.21$

**3.**

$\hat{p} = 0.39$ $\qquad$ $\hat{q} = 0.61$

$\hat{p} - (z_{\frac{\alpha}{2}})\sqrt{\frac{\hat{p}\hat{q}}{n}} < p < \hat{p} + (z_{\frac{\alpha}{2}})\sqrt{\frac{\hat{p}\hat{q}}{n}}$

$0.39 - (1.96)\sqrt{\frac{(0.39)(0.61)}{1500}} < p <$

$\qquad 0.39 + (1.96)\sqrt{\frac{(0.39)(0.61)}{1500}}$

$0.39 - 0.025 < p < 0.39 + 0.025$

$0.365 < p < 0.415$

**5.**

$\hat{p} = \frac{X}{n} = \frac{55}{450} = 0.12$

$\hat{q} = 1 - 0.12 = 0.88$

$\hat{p} - (z_{\frac{\alpha}{2}})\sqrt{\frac{\hat{p}\hat{q}}{n}} < p < \hat{p} + (z_{\frac{\alpha}{2}})\sqrt{\frac{\hat{p}\hat{q}}{n}}$

$0.12 - 1.96\sqrt{\frac{(0.12)(0.88)}{450}} < p < 0.12 + 1.96\sqrt{\frac{(0.12)(0.88)}{450}}$

$0.12 - 0.03 < p < 0.12 + 0.03$

$0.09$ or $9\% < p < 0.15$ or $15\%$

(Note: TI-83 answer is $0.092 < p < 0.153$)

11% is contained in the confidence interval.

**7.**

$\hat{p} = 0.84$ $\qquad$ $\hat{q} = 0.16$

$\hat{p} - (z_{\frac{\alpha}{2}})\sqrt{\frac{\hat{p}\hat{q}}{n}} < p < \hat{p} + (z_{\frac{\alpha}{2}})\sqrt{\frac{\hat{p}\hat{q}}{n}}$

$0.84 - 1.65\sqrt{\frac{(0.84)(0.16)}{200}} < p <$

$\qquad 0.84 + 1.65\sqrt{\frac{(0.84)(0.16)}{200}}$

$0.84 - 0.043 < p < 0.84 + 0.043$

$0.797 < p < 0.883$

**9.**

$\hat{p} = 0.23$ $\qquad$ $\hat{q} = 0.77$

$\hat{p} - (z_{\frac{\alpha}{2}})\sqrt{\frac{\hat{p}\hat{q}}{n}} < p < \hat{p} + (z_{\frac{\alpha}{2}})\sqrt{\frac{\hat{p}\hat{q}}{n}}$

$0.23 - 2.58\sqrt{\frac{(0.23)(0.77)}{200}} < p <$

$\qquad 0.23 + 2.58\sqrt{\frac{(0.23)(0.77)}{200}}$

$0.23 - 0.077 < p < 0.23 + 0.077$

$0.153 < p < 0.307$

The statement that one in five or 20% of 13 to 14 year olds is a sometime smoker is within the interval.

**11.**

$\hat{p} = \frac{36}{85} = 0.424$ $\quad$ $\hat{q} = \frac{49}{85} = 0.576$

$\hat{p} - (z_{\frac{\alpha}{2}})\sqrt{\frac{\hat{p}\hat{q}}{n}} < p < \hat{p} + (z_{\frac{\alpha}{2}})\sqrt{\frac{\hat{p}\hat{q}}{n}}$

$0.424 - 2.58\sqrt{\frac{(0.424)(0.576)}{85}} < p <$

$\qquad 0.424 + 2.58\sqrt{\frac{(0.424)(0.576)}{85}}$

$0.424 - 0.138 < p < 0.424 + 0.138$

$0.286 < p < 0.562$

It would not be considered larger since 0.52 is in the interval.

**13.**

$\hat{p} = 0.44975$ $\qquad$ $\hat{q} = 0.55025$

$\hat{p} - (z_{\frac{\alpha}{2}})\sqrt{\frac{\hat{p}\hat{q}}{n}} < p < \hat{p} + (z_{\frac{\alpha}{2}})\sqrt{\frac{\hat{p}\hat{q}}{n}}$

$0.44975 - 1.96\sqrt{\frac{(0.44975)(0.55025)}{1005}} < p <$

$\qquad 0.44975 + 1.96\sqrt{\frac{(0.44975)(0.55025)}{1005}}$

$0.44975 - 0.03076 < p <$

$\qquad\qquad 0.44975 + 0.03076$

$0.419 < p < 0.481$

**15.**

a. $\hat{p} = 0.25$ $\qquad$ $\hat{q} = 0.75$

$n = \hat{p}\,\hat{q}\left[\frac{z_{\frac{\alpha}{2}}}{E}\right]^2 = (0.25)(0.75)\left[\frac{2.58}{0.02}\right]^2$

$n = 3120.1875$ or $3121$

## 15. continued

b. $\hat{p} = 0.5$ $\qquad$ $\hat{q} = 0.5$

$n = \hat{p}\,\hat{q}\left[\dfrac{z_{\frac{\alpha}{2}}}{E}\right]^2 = (0.5)(0.5)\left[\dfrac{2.58}{0.02}\right]^2$

$n = 4160.25$ or $4161$

## 17.

a. $\hat{p} = \dfrac{30}{300} = 0.1$ $\hat{q} = \dfrac{270}{300} = 0.9$

$n = \hat{p}\,\hat{q}\left[\dfrac{z_{\frac{\alpha}{2}}}{E}\right]^2 = (0.1)(0.9)\left[\dfrac{1.65}{0.05}\right]^2$

$\quad = 98.01$ or $99$

b. $\hat{p} = 0.5$ $\qquad$ $\hat{q} = 0.5$

$n = \hat{p}\,\hat{q}\left[\dfrac{z_{\frac{\alpha}{2}}}{E}\right]^2 = (0.5)(0.5)\left[\dfrac{1.65}{0.05}\right]^2$

$n = 272.25$ or $273$

## 19.

$\hat{p} = 0.5$ $\qquad$ $\hat{q} = 0.5$

$n = \hat{p}\,\hat{q}\left[\dfrac{z_{\frac{\alpha}{2}}}{E}\right]^2$

$n = (0.5)(0.5)\left[\dfrac{1.96}{0.03}\right]^2$

$n = 1067.11$ or $1068$

## 21.

$600 = (0.5)(0.5)\left[\dfrac{z}{0.04}\right]^2$

$600 = 156.25 z^2$

$3.84 = z^2$

$\sqrt{3.84} = 1.96 = z$

1.96 corresponds to a 95% degree of confidence.

## EXERCISE SET 7-5

**1.**

$\chi^2$

**3.**

|    | $\chi^2_{\text{left}}$ | $\chi^2_{\text{right}}$ |
|----|--------|---------|
| a. | 3.816  | 21.920  |
| b. | 10.117 | 30.144  |
| c. | 13.844 | 41.923  |
| d. | 0.412  | 16.750  |
| e. | 26.509 | 55.758  |

**5.**

$\dfrac{(n-1)s^2}{\chi^2_{\text{right}}} < \sigma^2 < \dfrac{(n-1)s^2}{\chi^2_{\text{left}}}$

$\dfrac{22(3.8)^2}{36.781} < \sigma^2 < \dfrac{22(3.8)^2}{10.982}$

## 5. continued

$8.64 < \sigma^2 < 28.93$

$2.94 < \sigma < 5.38$

Yes. The times deviate between 3 and 5 minutes.

## 7.

$s^2 = 0.80997$ or $0.81$

$\dfrac{(n-1)s^2}{\chi^2_{\text{right}}} < \sigma^2 < \dfrac{(n-1)s^2}{\chi^2_{\text{left}}}$

$\dfrac{19(0.81)}{38.582} < \sigma^2 < \dfrac{19(0.81)}{6.844}$

$0.40 < \sigma^2 < 2.25$

$0.63 < \sigma < 1.50$

## 9.

$\dfrac{(n-1)s^2}{\chi^2_{\text{right}}} < \sigma^2 < \dfrac{(n-1)s^2}{\chi^2_{\text{left}}}$

$\dfrac{19(19.1913)^2}{30.144} < \sigma^2 < \dfrac{19(19.1913)^2}{10.117}$

$232.1 < \sigma^2 < 691.6$

$15.2 < \sigma < 26.3$

## 11.

$\dfrac{(n-1)s^2}{\chi^2_{\text{right}}} < \sigma^2 < \dfrac{(n-1)s^2}{\chi^2_{\text{left}}}$

$\dfrac{27(5.2)^2}{43.194} < \sigma^2 < \dfrac{27(5.2)^2}{14.573}$

$16.9 < \sigma^2 < 50.1$

$4.1 < \sigma < 7.1$

## 13.

$s - z_{\frac{\alpha}{2}}\left(\dfrac{s}{\sqrt{2n}}\right) < \sigma < s + z_{\frac{\alpha}{2}}\left(\dfrac{s}{\sqrt{2n}}\right)$

$18 - 1.96\left(\dfrac{18}{\sqrt{400}}\right) < \sigma < 18 + 1.96\left(\dfrac{18}{\sqrt{400}}\right)$

$16.2 < \sigma < 19.8$

## REVIEW EXERCISES - CHAPTER 7

**1.**

$\overline{X} = 7.8$ is the point estimate of $\mu$.

$\overline{X} - z_{\frac{\alpha}{2}}\left(\dfrac{s}{\sqrt{n}}\right) < \mu < \overline{X} + z_{\frac{\alpha}{2}}\left(\dfrac{s}{\sqrt{n}}\right)$

$7.8 - 1.65\left(\dfrac{0.6}{\sqrt{36}}\right) < \mu < 7.8 + 1.65\left(\dfrac{0.6}{\sqrt{36}}\right)$

$7.64 < \mu < 7.97$

The minimum speed should be about 7.64 miles per hour.

**3.**
$\overline{X} = 7.5$ is the point estimate of $\mu$.

$$\overline{X} - z_{\frac{\alpha}{2}}\left(\frac{s}{\sqrt{n}}\right) < \mu < \overline{X} + z_{\frac{\alpha}{2}}\left(\frac{s}{\sqrt{n}}\right)$$

$$7.5 - 1.96\left(\frac{0.8}{\sqrt{1500}}\right) < \mu < 7.5 + 1.96\left(\frac{0.8}{\sqrt{1500}}\right)$$

$$7.46 < \mu < 7.54$$

**5.**
$$\overline{X} - t_{\frac{\alpha}{2}}\left(\frac{s}{\sqrt{n}}\right) < \mu < \overline{X} + t_{\frac{\alpha}{2}}\left(\frac{s}{\sqrt{n}}\right)$$

$$28 - 2.132\left(\frac{3}{\sqrt{5}}\right) < \mu < 28 + 2.132\left(\frac{3}{\sqrt{5}}\right)$$

$$25 < \mu < 31$$

**7.**
$$n = \left[\frac{z_{\frac{\alpha}{2}}\,\sigma}{E}\right]^2 = \left[\frac{1.65(80)}{25}\right]^2$$

$$= (5.28)^2 = 27.88 \text{ or } 28$$

**9.**
$$\hat{p} = 0.547 \qquad \hat{q} = 0.453$$

$$\hat{p} - (z_{\frac{\alpha}{2}})\sqrt{\frac{\hat{p}\hat{q}}{n}} < p < \hat{p} + (z_{\frac{\alpha}{2}})\sqrt{\frac{\hat{p}\hat{q}}{n}}$$

$$0.547 - 1.96\sqrt{\frac{(0.547)(0.453)}{75}} < p <$$
$$0.547 + 1.96\sqrt{\frac{(0.547)(0.453)}{75}}$$

$0.547 - 0.113 < p < 0.547 + 0.113$
$0.434 < p < 0.660$
Yes; it seems that as many as 66% were dissatisfied.

**11.**
$$\hat{p} = 0.88 \qquad \hat{q} = 0.12$$

$$n = \hat{p}\,\hat{q}\left[\frac{z_{\frac{\alpha}{2}}}{E}\right]^2 = (0.88)(0.12)\left[\frac{1.65}{0.025}\right]^2$$

$$n = 459.99 \text{ or } 460$$

**13.**
$$\frac{(n-1)s^2}{\chi^2_{right}} < \sigma^2 < \frac{(n-1)s^2}{\chi^2_{left}}$$

$$\frac{(18-1)(0.29)^2}{30.191} < \sigma^2 < \frac{(18-1)(0.29)^2}{7.564}$$

$0.0474 < \sigma^2 < 0.1890$
$0.218 < \sigma < 0.435$

**13. continued**
Yes; it seems that there is a large standard deviation.

**15.**
$$\frac{(n-1)s^2}{\chi^2_{right}} < \sigma^2 < \frac{(n-1)s^2}{\chi^2_{left}}$$

$$\frac{(15-1)(8.6)}{23.685} < \sigma^2 < \frac{(15-1)(8.6)}{6.571}$$

$$5.1 < \sigma^2 < 18.3$$

## CHAPTER 7 QUIZ

1. True
2. True
3. False, it is consistent if, as sample size increases, the estimator approaches the parameter being estimated.
4. True
5. b
6. a
7. b
8. Unbiased, consistent, relatively efficient
9. Maximum error of estimate
10. Point
11. 90, 95, 99

**12.**
$\overline{X} = \$23.45$ is the point estimate for $\mu$.
$$\overline{X} - z_{\frac{\alpha}{2}}\left(\frac{s}{\sqrt{n}}\right) < \mu < \overline{X} + z_{\frac{\alpha}{2}}\left(\frac{s}{\sqrt{n}}\right)$$

$$\$23.45 - 1.65\left(\frac{2.80}{\sqrt{49}}\right) < \mu <$$
$$\$23.45 + 1.65\left(\frac{2.80}{\sqrt{49}}\right)$$

$$\$22.79 < \mu < \$24.11$$

**13.**
$\overline{X} = \$44.80$ is the point estimate for $\mu$.

$$\overline{X} - t_{\frac{\alpha}{2}}\left(\frac{s}{\sqrt{n}}\right) < \mu < \overline{X} + t_{\frac{\alpha}{2}}\left(\frac{s}{\sqrt{n}}\right)$$

$$\$44.80 - 2.093\left(\frac{3.53}{\sqrt{20}}\right) < \mu <$$
$$\$44.80 + 2.093\left(\frac{3.53}{\sqrt{20}}\right)$$

$$\$43.15 < \mu < \$46.45$$

**14.**
$\overline{X} = 4150$ is the point estimate for $\mu$.

$$\overline{X} - z_{\frac{\alpha}{2}}\left(\frac{s}{\sqrt{n}}\right) < \mu < \overline{X} + z_{\frac{\alpha}{2}}\left(\frac{s}{\sqrt{n}}\right)$$

14. continued

$$\$4150 - 2.58\left(\frac{480}{\sqrt{40}}\right) < \mu <$$
$$\$4150 + 2.58\left(\frac{480}{\sqrt{40}}\right)$$

$$\$3954 < \mu < \$4346$$

15.

$$\overline{X} - t_{\frac{\alpha}{2}}\left(\frac{s}{\sqrt{n}}\right) < \mu < \overline{X} + t_{\frac{\alpha}{2}}\left(\frac{s}{\sqrt{n}}\right)$$

$$48.6 - 2.262\left(\frac{4.1}{\sqrt{10}}\right) < \mu < 48.6 + 2.262\left(\frac{4.1}{\sqrt{10}}\right)$$

$$45.7 < \mu < 51.5$$

16.

$$\overline{X} - t_{\frac{\alpha}{2}}\left(\frac{s}{\sqrt{n}}\right) < \mu < \overline{X} + t_{\frac{\alpha}{2}}\left(\frac{s}{\sqrt{n}}\right)$$

$$438 - 3.499\left(\frac{16}{\sqrt{8}}\right) < \mu < 438 + 3.499\left(\frac{16}{\sqrt{8}}\right)$$

$$418 < \mu < 458$$

17.

$$\overline{X} - t_{\frac{\alpha}{2}}\left(\frac{s}{\sqrt{n}}\right) < \mu < \overline{X} + t_{\frac{\alpha}{2}}\left(\frac{s}{\sqrt{n}}\right)$$

$$31 - 2.353\left(\frac{4}{\sqrt{4}}\right) < \mu < 31 + 2.353\left(\frac{4}{\sqrt{4}}\right)$$

$$26 < \mu < 36$$

18.

$$n = \left[\frac{z_{\frac{\alpha}{2}}\,\sigma}{E}\right]^2 = \left[\frac{2.58(2.6)}{0.5}\right]^2$$

$$= 179.98 \text{ or } 180$$

19.

$$n = \left[\frac{z_{\frac{\alpha}{2}}\,\sigma}{E}\right]^2 = \left[\frac{1.65(900)}{300}\right]^2$$

$$= 24.5 \text{ or } 25$$

20.

$$\hat{p} - (z_{\frac{\alpha}{2}})\sqrt{\frac{\hat{p}\hat{q}}{n}} < p < \hat{p} + (z_{\frac{\alpha}{2}})\sqrt{\frac{\hat{p}\hat{q}}{n}}$$

$$\hat{p} = \frac{53}{75} = 0.707 \quad \hat{q} = \frac{22}{75} = 0.293$$

$$0.71 - 1.96\sqrt{\frac{(0.707)(0.293)}{75}} < p <$$
$$0.71 + 1.96\sqrt{\frac{(0.707)(0.293)}{75}}$$

$$0.604 < p < 0.810$$

21.

$$\hat{p} - (z_{\frac{\alpha}{2}})\sqrt{\frac{\hat{p}\hat{q}}{n}} < p < \hat{p} + (z_{\frac{\alpha}{2}})\sqrt{\frac{\hat{p}\hat{q}}{n}}$$

$$0.36 - 1.65\sqrt{\frac{(0.36)(0.64)}{150}} < p <$$
$$0.36 + 1.65\sqrt{\frac{(0.36)(0.64)}{150}}$$

$$0.295 < p < 0.425$$

22.

$$\hat{p} - (z_{\frac{\alpha}{2}})\sqrt{\frac{\hat{p}\hat{q}}{n}} < p < \hat{p} + (z_{\frac{\alpha}{2}})\sqrt{\frac{\hat{p}\hat{q}}{n}}$$

$$0.4444 - 1.96\sqrt{\frac{(0.4444)(0.5556)}{90}} < p <$$
$$0.4444 + 1.96\sqrt{\frac{(0.4444)(0.5556)}{90}}$$

$$0.342 < p < 0.547$$

23.

$$n = \hat{p}\,\hat{q}\left[\frac{z_{\frac{\alpha}{2}}}{E}\right]^2$$

$$= (0.15)(0.85)\left[\frac{1.96}{0.03}\right]^2$$

$$= 544.22 \text{ or } 545$$

24.

$$\frac{(n-1)s^2}{\chi^2_{\text{right}}} < \sigma^2 < \frac{(n-1)s^2}{\chi^2_{\text{left}}}$$

$$\frac{24(9)^2}{39.364} < \sigma^2 < \frac{24(9)^2}{12.401}$$

$$49.4 < \sigma^2 < 156.8$$
$$7 < \sigma < 13$$

25.

$$\frac{(n-1)s^2}{\chi^2_{\text{right}}} < \sigma^2 < \frac{(n-1)s^2}{\chi^2_{\text{left}}}$$

$$\frac{26(6.8)^2}{38.885} < \sigma^2 < \frac{26(6.8)^2}{15.379}$$

$$30.9 < \sigma^2 < 78.2$$
$$5.6 < \sigma < 8.8$$

26.

$$\frac{(n-1)s^2}{\chi^2_{\text{right}}} < \sigma^2 < \frac{(n-1)s^2}{\chi^2_{\text{left}}}$$

$$\frac{19(2.3)^2}{30.144} < \sigma^2 < \frac{19(2.3)^2}{10.177}$$

$$3.33 < \sigma^2 < 10$$
$$1.8 < \sigma < 3.2$$

Note: Graphs are not to scale and are intended to convey a general idea. Answers may vary due to rounding.

**EXERCISE SET 8-2**

**1.**
The null hypothesis is a statistical hypothesis that states there is no difference between a parameter and a specific value or there is no difference between two parameters. The alternative hypothesis specifies a specific difference between a parameter and a specific value, or that there is a difference between two parameters. Examples will vary.

**3.**
A statistical test uses the data obtained from a sample to make a decision as to whether or not the null hypothesis should be rejected.

**5.**
The critical region is the region of values of the test-statistic that indicates a significant difference and the null hypothesis should be rejected. The non-critical region is the region of values of the test-statistic that indicates the difference was probably due to chance, and the null hypothesis should not be rejected.

**7.**
Type I is represented by $\alpha$, type II is represented by $\beta$.

**9.**
A one-tailed test should be used when a specific direction, such as greater than or less than, is being hypothesized, whereas when no direction is specified, a two-tailed test should be used.

**11.**
Hypotheses can only be proved true when the entire population is used to compute the test statistic. In most cases, this is impossible.

**12.**
a.  $\pm 1.96$

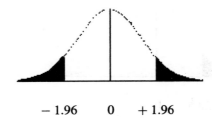

$-1.96 \qquad 0 \qquad +1.96$

b.  $-2.33$

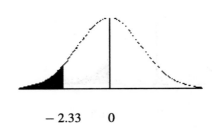

$-2.33 \qquad 0$

c.  $+2.58$

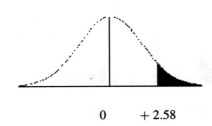

$0 \qquad +2.58$

d.  $+2.33$

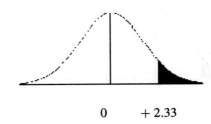

$0 \qquad +2.33$

e.  $-1.65$

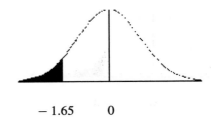

$-1.65 \qquad 0$

## 12. continued
f.  − 2.05

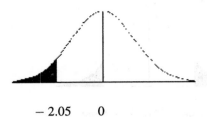

− 2.05    0

g.  + 1.65

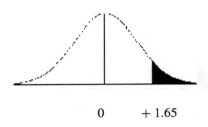

0    + 1.65

h.  ± 2.58

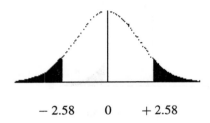

− 2.58    0    + 2.58

i.  − 1.75

− 1.75    0

j.  + 2.05

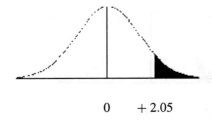

0    + 2.05

## 13.
a.  $H_0$: $\mu = 24.6$
   $H_1$: $\mu \neq 24.6$

b.  $H_0$: $\mu = \$51,497$
   $H_1$: $\mu \neq \$51,497$

c.  $H_0$: $\mu \leq 25.4$
   $H_1$: $\mu > 25.4$

d.  $H_0$: $\mu \geq 88$
   $H_1$: $\mu < 88$

e.  $H_0$: $\mu \geq 70$
   $H_1$: $\mu < 70$

f.  $H_0$: $\mu = \$79.95$
   $H_1$: $\mu \neq \$79.95$

g.  $H_0$: $\mu = 8.2$
   $H_1$: $\mu \neq 8.2$

## EXERCISE SET 8-3

1.
$H_0$: $\mu = \$69.21$    (claim)
$H_1$: $\mu \neq \$69.21$

C. V. $= \pm 1.96$
$z = \frac{\overline{X}-\mu}{\frac{\sigma}{\sqrt{n}}} = \frac{\$68.43-\$69.21}{\frac{3.72}{\sqrt{30}}} = -1.15$

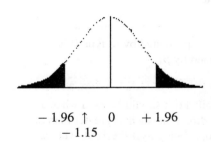

− 1.96 ↑    0    + 1.96
− 1.15

Do not reject the null hypothesis. There is not enough evidence to reject the claim that the average cost of a hotel stay in Atlanta is $69.21.

3.
$H_0$: $\mu \leq \$24$ billion
$H1$: $\mu > \$24$ billion    (claim)

C. V. $= + 1.65$    $\overline{X} = \$31.5$    $s = \$28.7$
$z = \frac{\overline{X}-\mu}{\frac{\sigma}{\sqrt{n}}} = \frac{31.5-24}{\frac{28.7}{\sqrt{50}}} = 1.85$

**3. continued**

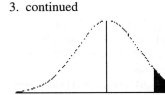

0    1.65    ↑
              1.85

Reject the null hypothesis. There is enough evidence to support the claim that the average revenue exceeds $24 billion.

**5.**
$H_0$: $\mu \geq 14$
$H_1$: $\mu < 14$    (claim)

C. V. $= -2.33$
$z = \frac{\overline{X}-\mu}{\frac{s}{\sqrt{n}}} = \frac{11.8-14}{\frac{2.7}{\sqrt{36}}} = -4.89$

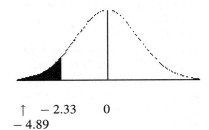

↑   $-2.33$    0
$-4.89$

Reject the null hypothesis. There is enough evidence to support the claim that the average age of the planes in the executive's airline is less than the national average.

**7.**
$H_0$: $\mu = 29$
$H_1$: $\mu \neq 29$    (claim)

C. V. $= \pm 1.96$    $\overline{X} = 29.45$    $s = 2.61$
$z = \frac{\overline{X}-\mu}{\frac{\sigma}{\sqrt{n}}} = \frac{29.45-29}{\frac{2.61}{\sqrt{30}}} = 0.944$

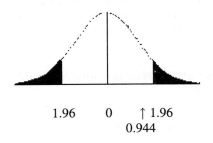

1.96    0    ↑ 1.96
              0.944

**7. continued**
Do not reject the null hypothesis. There is enough evidence to reject the claim that the average height differs from 29 inches.

**9.**
$H_0$: $\mu \leq \$19,410$
$H_1$: $\mu > \$19,410$    (claim)

C. V. $= 2.33$
$z = \frac{\overline{X}-\mu}{\frac{\sigma}{\sqrt{n}}} = \frac{\$22,098-\$19,410}{\frac{6050}{\sqrt{40}}} = 2.81$

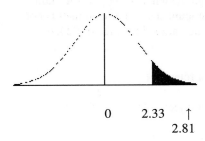

0    2.33    ↑
              2.81

Reject the null hypothesis. There is enough evidence to support the claim that the average tuition cost has increased.

**11.**
$H_0$: $\mu = 125$
$H_1$: $\mu \neq 125$    (claim)

C. V. $= \pm 2.58$
$z = \frac{\overline{X}-\mu}{\frac{\sigma}{\sqrt{n}}} = \frac{110-125}{\frac{30}{\sqrt{35}}} = -2.96$

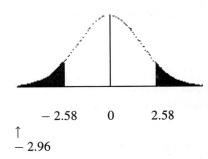

$-2.58$    0    2.58
↑
$-2.96$

Reject the null hypothesis. There is enough evidence to support the claim that the average number of guests differs from 125.

**13.**
$H_0$: $\mu = \$24.44$
$H_1$: $\mu \neq \$24.44$    (claim)

C. V. $= \pm 2.33$
$z = \frac{\overline{X}-\mu}{\frac{s}{\sqrt{n}}} = \frac{22.97-24.44}{\frac{3.70}{\sqrt{33}}} = -2.28$

13. continued

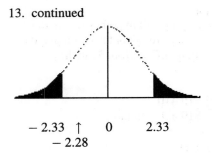

$-2.33 \uparrow \quad 0 \quad 2.33$
$\quad -2.28$

Do not reject the null hypothesis. There is not enough evidence to support the claim that the amount spent at a local mall is not equal to the national average of $24.44.

15.
a. Do not reject.
b. Reject.
c. Do not reject.
d. Reject
e. Reject

17.
$H_0$: $\mu \geq 264$
$H_1$: $\mu < 264$ (claim)
$z = \frac{\overline{X}-\mu}{\frac{\sigma}{\sqrt{n}}} = \frac{262.3-264}{\frac{3}{\sqrt{20}}} = -2.53$

The area corresponding to z = 2.53 is 0.4943. The P-value is $0.5 - 0.4943 = 0.0057$. The decision is to reject the null hypothesis since $0.0057 < 0.01$. There is enough evidence to support the claim that the average stopping distance is less than 264 feet.

19.
$H_0$: $\mu \geq 546$
$H_1$: $\mu < 546$ (claim)
$z = \frac{\overline{X}-\mu}{\frac{\sigma}{\sqrt{n}}} = \frac{544.8-546}{\frac{3}{\sqrt{36}}} = -2.4$

The area corresponding to z $= -2.4$ is 0.4918. The P-value is $0.5 - 0.4918 = 0.0082$. The decision is to reject the null hypothesis since $0.0082 < 0.01$. There is enough evidence to support the claim that the number of calories burned is less than 546.

21.
$H_0$: $\mu \geq 47.1$
$H_1$: $\mu < 47.1$ (claim)
$z = \frac{\overline{X}-\mu}{\frac{\sigma}{\sqrt{n}}} = \frac{43.2-47.1}{\frac{8.6}{\sqrt{50}}} = -3.21$

21. continued
The area corresponding to z = 3.21 is $+0.4999$. To get the P-value, subtract 0.4999 from 0.5 and then multiply by 2 since this is a two-tailed test.
$2(0.5 - 0.4999) = 2(0.0001) = 0.0002$. thus the P-value is less than 0.0002.
The decision is to reject the null hypothesis since P-value $< 0.01$. There is enough evidence to support the claim that the mean is less than 47.1 acres.

23.
$H_0$: $\mu = 30,000$ (claim)
$H_1$: $\mu \neq 30,000$
$z = \frac{\overline{X}-\mu}{\frac{s}{\sqrt{n}}} = \frac{30,456-30,000}{\frac{1684}{\sqrt{40}}} = 1.71$

The area corresponding to z = 1.71 is 0.4564. The P-value is $2(0.5 - 0.4564) = 2(0.0436) = 0.0872$. The decision is to reject the null hypothesis at $\alpha = 0.10$ since $0.0872 < 0.10$. The conclusion is that there is enough evidence to reject the claim that customers are adhering to the recommendation. A 0.10 significance level is probably appropriate since there is little consequence of a Type I error. The dealer would be advised to increase efforts to make its customers aware of the service recommendation.

25.
$H_0$: $\mu \geq 10$
$H_1$: $\mu < 10$ (claim)

$\overline{X} = 5.025 \quad s = 3.63$
$z = \frac{\overline{X}-\mu}{\frac{s}{\sqrt{n}}} = \frac{5.025-10}{\frac{3.63}{\sqrt{40}}} = -8.67$

The area corresponding to 8.67 is greater than 0.4999. The P-value is $0.5 - 0.4999 < 0.0001$. Since $0.0001 < 0.05$, the decision is to reject the null hypothesis. There is enough evidence to support the claim that the average number of days missed per year is less than 10.

27.
The mean and standard deviation are found as follows:

27. continued

| | f | $X_m$ | $f \cdot X_m$ | $f \cdot X_m^2$ |
|---|---|---|---|---|
| 8.35 - 8.43 | 2 | 8.39 | 16.78 | 140.7842 |
| 8.44 - 8.52 | 6 | 8.48 | 50.88 | 431.4624 |
| 8.53 - 8.61 | 12 | 8.57 | 102.84 | 881.3388 |
| 8.62 - 8.70 | 18 | 8.66 | 155.88 | 1349.9208 |
| 8.71 - 8.79 | 10 | 8.75 | 87.5 | 765.625 |
| 8.80 - 8.88 | 2 | 8.84 | 17.68 | 156.2912 |
| | 50 | | 431.56 | 3725.4224 |

$$\overline{X} = \frac{\sum f \cdot X_m}{n} = \frac{431.56}{50} = 8.63$$

$$s = \sqrt{\frac{\sum f \cdot X_m^2 - \frac{\sum (f \cdot X_m)^2}{n}}{n-1}} = \sqrt{\frac{3725.4224 - \frac{(431.56)^2}{50}}{49}}$$

$$= 0.105$$

$H_0: \mu = 8.65$ (claim)
$H_1: \mu \neq 8.65$

C. V. $= \pm 1.96$
$$z = \frac{\overline{X} - \mu}{\frac{s}{\sqrt{n}}} = \frac{8.63 - 8.65}{\frac{0.105}{\sqrt{50}}} = -1.35$$

Do not reject the null hypothesis. There is not enough evidence to reject the claim that the average hourly wage of the employees is $8.65.

EXERCISE SET 8-4

1.
It is bell-shaped, symmetric about the mean, and it never touches the x axis. The mean, median, and mode are all equal to 0 and they are located at the center of the distribution. The t distribution differs from the standard normal distribution in that it is a family of curves, the variance is greater than one, and as the degrees of freedom increase the t distribution approaches the standard normal distribution.

3.
a. d. f. $= 9$     C. V. $= +1.833$
b. d. f. $= 17$    C. V. $= \pm 1.740$
c. d. f. $= 5$     C. V. $= -3.365$
d. d. f. $= 8$     C. V. $= +2.306$
e. d. f. $= 14$    C. V. $= \pm 2.145$
f. d. f. $= 22$    C. V. $= -2.819$
g. d. f. $= 27$    C. V. $= \pm 2.771$
h. d. f. $= 16$    C. V. $= \pm 2.583$

4.
a. $0.01 <$ P-value $< 0.025$ (0.018)
b. $0.05 <$ P-value $< 0.10$ (0.062)
c. $0.10 <$ P-value $< 0.25$ (0.123)
d. $0.10 <$ P-value $< 0.20$ (0.138)
e. P-value $< 0.005$        (0.003)
f. $0.10 <$ P-value $< 0.25$ (0.158)
g. P-value $= 0.05$       (0.05)
h. P-value $> 0.25$       (0.261)

5.
$H_0: \mu \geq 11.52$
$H_1: \mu < 11.52$ (claim)

C. V. $= -1.833$    d. f. $= 9$

$$t = \frac{\overline{X} - \mu}{\frac{s}{\sqrt{n}}} = \frac{7.42 - 11.52}{\frac{1.3}{\sqrt{10}}} = -9.97$$

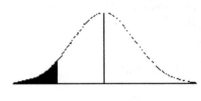

$\uparrow$   $-1.833$      0
$-9.97$

Reject the null hypothesis. There is enough evidence to support the claim that the rainfall is below average.

6.
$H_0: \mu \geq 2000$
$H_1: \mu < 2000$ (claim)

C. V. $= -3.747$    d. f. $= 4$
$\overline{X} = 1885.8$    $s = 2456.3$
$$t = \frac{\overline{X} - \mu}{\frac{s}{\sqrt{n}}} = \frac{1885.8 - 2000}{\frac{2456.3}{\sqrt{5}}} = -0.104$$

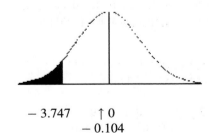

$-3.747$     $\uparrow 0$
$-0.104$

Do not reject the null hypothesis. There is not enough evidence to support the claim that the average acreage is less than 2000.

7.

$H_0$: $\mu = \$40,000$

$H_1$: $\mu \neq \$40,000$   (claim)

C. V. $= \pm 2.093$   d. f. $= 19$

$t = \dfrac{\overline{X} - \mu}{\frac{s}{\sqrt{n}}} = \dfrac{43,228 - 40,000}{\frac{4000}{\sqrt{20}}} = 3.61$

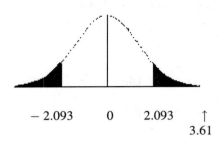

$-2.093$   $0$   $2.093$   $\uparrow$
$3.61$

Reject the null hypothesis. There is enough evidence to support the claim that the average salary is not $40,000.

9.

$H_0$: $\mu \geq 700$   (claim)

$H_1$: $\mu < 700$

$\overline{X} = 606.5$   $s = 109.1$

C. V. $= -2.262$   d. f. $= 9$

$t = \dfrac{\overline{X} - \mu}{\frac{s}{\sqrt{n}}} = \dfrac{606.5 - 700}{\frac{109.1}{\sqrt{10}}} = -2.71$

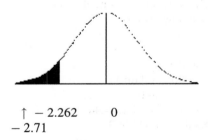

$\uparrow -2.262$   $0$
$-2.71$

Reject the null hypothesis. There is enough evidence to reject the claim that the average height of the buildings is at least 700 feet.

11.

$H_0$: $\mu \leq \$13,252$

$H_1$: $\mu > \$13,252$   (claim)

C. V. $= 2.539$   d. f. $= 19$

$t = \dfrac{\overline{X} - \mu}{\frac{s}{\sqrt{n}}} = \dfrac{\$15,560 - \$13,252}{\frac{\$3500}{\sqrt{20}}} = 2.949$

11.  continued

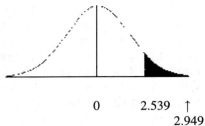

$0$   $2.539$   $\uparrow$
$2.949$

Reject the null hypothesis. There is enough evidence to support the claim that the average tuition cost has increased.

13.

$H_0$: $\mu \leq \$54.8$

$H_1$: $\mu > \$54.8$   (claim)

C. V. $= 1.761$   d. f. $= 14$

$t = \dfrac{\overline{X} - \mu}{\frac{s}{\sqrt{n}}} = \dfrac{\$62.3 - \$54.8}{\frac{\$9.5}{\sqrt{15}}} = 3.058$

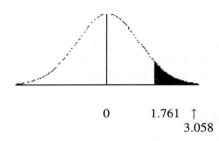

$0$   $1.761$   $\uparrow$
$3.058$

Reject the null hypothesis. There is enough evidence to support the claim that the cost to produce an action movie is more than $54.8 million.

15.

$H_0$: $\mu = 132$ min.   (claim)

$H_1$: $\mu \neq 132$ min.

C. V. $= \pm 2.365$   d. f. $= 7$

$t = \dfrac{\overline{X} - \mu}{\frac{s}{\sqrt{n}}} = \dfrac{125 - 132}{\frac{11}{\sqrt{8}}} = -1.7999$

Do not reject the null hypothesis. There is enough evidence to support the claim that the average show time is 132 minutes, or 2 hours and 12 minutes.

17.

$H_0$: $\mu = 5.8$

$H_1$: $\mu \neq 5.8$   (claim)

$\overline{X} = 3.85$   $s = 2.52$

d. f. $= 19$   $\alpha = 0.05$

17. continued
P-value < 0.01    (0.0026)
$t = \frac{\overline{X}-\mu}{\frac{s}{\sqrt{n}}} = \frac{3.85-5.8}{\frac{2.52}{\sqrt{20}}} = -3.46$

Since P-value < 0.01, reject the null hypothesis. There is enough evidence to support the claim that the mean has changed.

19.
$H_0$: $\mu = \$15,000$
$H_1$: $\mu \neq \$15,000$    (claim)

$\overline{X} = \$14,347.17$    $s = \$2048.54$
d. f. = 11    C. V. = $\pm 2.201$

$t = \frac{\overline{X}-\mu}{\frac{s}{\sqrt{n}}} = \frac{\$14,347.17-\$15,000}{\frac{\$2048.54}{\sqrt{12}}} = -1.10$

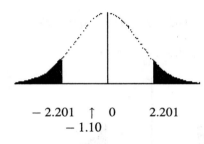

$-2.201$    ↑    0        2.201
        $-1.10$

Do not reject the null hypothesis. There is not enough evidence to say that the average stipend differs from $15,000.

EXERCISE SET 8-5

1.
Answers will vary.

3.
$np \geq 5$ and $nq \geq 5$

5.
$H_0$: $p = 0.647$
$H_1$: $p \neq 0.647$    (claim)

$\hat{p} = \frac{92}{150} = 0.613$    $p = 0.647$    $q = 0.353$
C. V. = $\pm 2.58$

$z = \frac{\hat{p}-p}{\sqrt{\frac{pq}{n}}} = \frac{0.613-0.647}{\sqrt{\frac{(0.647)(0.353)}{150}}} = -0.86$

5. continued

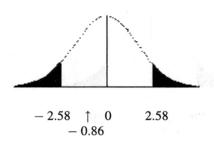

$-2.58$    ↑    0        2.58
        $-0.86$

Do not reject the null hypothesis. There is not enough evidence to support the claim that the proportion of homeowners is different from 0.647.

7.
$H_0$: $p = 0.40$
$H_1$: $p \neq 0.40$    (claim)

$\hat{p} = \frac{65}{180} = 0.361$    $p = 0.40$    $q = 0.60$
C. V. = $\pm 2.58$
$z = \frac{\hat{p}-p}{\sqrt{\frac{pq}{n}}} = \frac{0.361-0.40}{\sqrt{\frac{(0.40)(0.60)}{180}}} = -1.07$

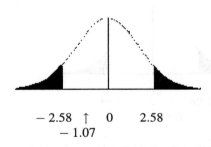

$-2.58$    ↑    0        2.58
        $-1.07$

Do not reject the null hypothesis. There is not enough evidence to conclude that the proportion differs from 0.40.

9.
$H_0$: $p = 0.63$    (claim)
$H_1$: $p \neq 0.63$

$\hat{p} = \frac{85}{143} = 0.5944$    $p = 0.63$    $q = 0.37$
C. V. = $\pm 1.96$
$z = \frac{\hat{p}-p}{\sqrt{\frac{pq}{n}}} = \frac{0.5944-0.63}{\sqrt{\frac{(0.63)(0.37)}{143}}} = -0.88$

9. continued

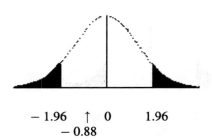

$$-1.96 \quad \uparrow \quad 0 \quad 1.96$$
$$-0.88$$

Do not reject the null hypothesis. There is not enough evidence to reject the claim that the percentage is the same.

11.
$H_0$: $p = 0.54$
$H_1$: $p \neq 0.54$ (claim)

$\hat{p} = \frac{14}{30} = 0.4667 \quad p = 0.54 \quad q = 0.46$
C. V. $= \pm 1.96$
$z = \frac{\hat{p}-p}{\sqrt{\frac{pq}{n}}} = \frac{0.4667-0.54}{\sqrt{\frac{(0.54)(0.46)}{30}}} = -0.81$

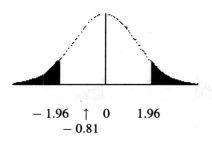

$$-1.96 \quad \uparrow \quad 0 \quad 1.96$$
$$-0.81$$

Do not reject the null hypothesis. There is not enough evidence to reject the claim that 54% of fatal car/truck accidents are caused by driver error.

13.
$H_0$: $p = 0.54$ (claim)
$H_1$: $p \neq 0.54$

$\hat{p} = \frac{36}{60} = 0.6 \quad p = 0.54 \quad q = 0.46$
$z = \frac{\hat{p}-p}{\sqrt{\frac{pq}{n}}} = \frac{0.6-0.54}{\sqrt{\frac{(0.54)(0.46)}{60}}} = 0.93$
Area $= 0.3238$
P-value $= 2(0.5 - 0.3238) = 0.3524$
Do not reject the null hypothesis. There is not enough evidence to reject the claim that 54% of kids had a snack after school. Yes, a healthy snack should be made available for children to eat after school.

15.
$H_0$: $p = 0.18$ (claim)
$H_1$: $p \neq 0.18$

$\hat{p} = \frac{50}{300} = 0.1667 \quad p = 0.18 \quad q = 0.82$
$z = \frac{\hat{p}-p}{\sqrt{\frac{pq}{n}}} = \frac{0.1667-0.18}{\sqrt{\frac{(0.18)(0.82)}{300}}} = -0.60$
Area $= 0.2257$
P-value $= 2(0.5 - 0.2257) = 0.5486$
Since P-value $> 0.05$, do not reject the null hypothesis. There is not enough evidence to reject the claim that 18% of all high school students smoke at least a pack of cigarettes a day.

17.
$H_0$: $p = 0.67$
$H_1$: $p \neq 0.67$ (claim)

$\hat{p} = \frac{82}{100} = 0.82 \quad p = 0.67 \quad q = 0.33$
C. V. $= \pm 1.96$
$z = \frac{\hat{p}-p}{\sqrt{\frac{pq}{n}}} = \frac{0.82-0.67}{\sqrt{\frac{(0.67)(0.33)}{100}}} = 3.19$

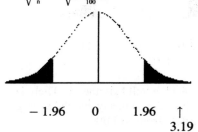

$$-1.96 \quad 0 \quad 1.96 \quad \uparrow$$
$$3.19$$

Reject the null hypothesis. There is enough evidence to support the claim that the percentage is not 67%.

19.
$H_0$: $p \geq 0.576$
$H_1$: $p < 0.576$ (claim)

$\hat{p} = \frac{17}{36} = 0.472 \quad p = 0.576 \quad q = 0.424$
C. V. $= -1.65$
$z = \frac{\hat{p}-p}{\sqrt{\frac{pq}{n}}} = \frac{0.472-0.576}{\sqrt{\frac{(0.576)(0.424)}{36}}} = -1.26$

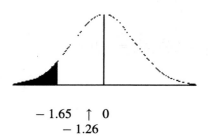

$$-1.65 \quad \uparrow \quad 0$$
$$-1.26$$

**19. continued**
Do not reject the null hypothesis. There is not enough evidence to support the claim that the percentage of injuries during practice is below 57.6%.

**21.**
This represents a binomial distribution with $p = 0.50$ and $n = 9$. The P-value is $2 \cdot P(X \leq 3) = 2(0.254) = 0.508$. Since P-value $> 0.10$, the conclusion that the coin is not balanced is probably false.

**23.**
$$z = \frac{X - \mu}{\sigma}$$

$$z = \frac{X - np}{\sqrt{npq}} \text{ since } \mu = np \text{ and } \sigma = \sqrt{npq}$$

$$z = \frac{\frac{X}{n} - \frac{np}{n}}{\frac{1}{n}\sqrt{npq}}$$

$$z = \frac{\frac{X}{n} - \frac{np}{n}}{\sqrt{\frac{npq}{n^2}}}$$

$$z = \frac{\hat{p} - p}{\sqrt{\frac{pq}{n}}} \text{ since } \hat{p} = \frac{X}{n}$$

**EXERCISE SET 8-6**

**1.**
a. $H_0$: $\sigma^2 \leq 225$
   $H_1$: $\sigma^2 > 225$

C. V. $= 27.587$     d. f. $= 17$

0                  27.587

b. $H_0$: $\sigma^2 \geq 225$
   $H_1$: $\sigma^2 < 225$

C. V. $= 14.042$     d. f. $= 22$

**1b. continued**

0    14.042

c. $H_0$: $\sigma^2 = 225$
   $H_1$: $\sigma^2 \neq 225$

C. V. $= 5.629, 26.119$     d. f. $= 14$

0    5.629                    26.119

d. $H_0$: $\sigma^2 = 225$
   $H_1$: $\sigma^2 \neq 225$

C. V. $= 2.167, 14.067$     d. f. $= 7$

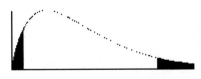

0    2.167                    14.067

e. $H_0$: $\sigma^2 \leq 225$
   $H_1$: $\sigma^2 > 225$

C. V. $= 32.000$     d. f. $= 16$

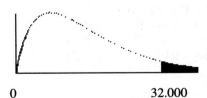

0                    32.000

f. $H_0$: $\sigma^2 \geq 225$
   $H_1$: $\sigma^2 < 225$

C. V. $= 8.907$     d. f. $= 19$

## 1f. continued

0   8.907

g. $H_0$: $\sigma^2 = 225$
    $H_1$: $\sigma^2 \neq 225$

C. V. = 3.074, 28.299    d. f. = 12

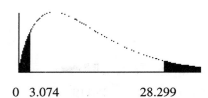

0   3.074                    28.299

h. $H_0$: $\sigma^2 \geq 225$
    $H_1$: $\sigma^2 < 225$

C. V. = 15.308    d. f. = 28

0   15.308

## 2.
a. $0.01 < $ P-value $< 0.025$    (0.015)
b. $0.005 < $ P-value $< 0.01$    (0.006)
c. $0.01 < $ P-value $< 0.025$    (0.012)
d. P-value $< 0.005$            (0.003)
e. $0.025 < $ P-value $< 0.05$    (0.037)
f. $0.05 < $ P-value $< 0.10$    (0.088)
g. $0.05 < $ P-value $< 0.10$    (0.066)
h. P-value $< 0.01$            (0.007)

## 3.
$H_0$: $\sigma = 60$        (claim)
$H_1$: $\sigma \neq 60$

C. V. = 8.672, 27.587    $\alpha = 0.10$
d. f. = 17
s = 64.6
$\chi^2 = \frac{(n-1)s^2}{\sigma^2} = \frac{(18-1)(64.6)^2}{(60)^2} = 19.707$

## 3. continued

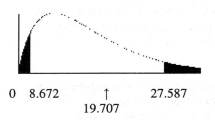

0   8.672              ↑              27.587
                       19.707

Do not reject the null hypothesis. There is not enough evidence to reject the claim that the standard deviation is 60.

## 5.
$H_0$: $\sigma \geq 15$
$H_1$: $\sigma < 15$    (claim)

C. V. = 4.575    $\alpha = 0.05$    d. f. = 14

$\chi^2 = \frac{(n-1)s^2}{\sigma^2} = \frac{(15-1)(13.6)^2}{15^2} = 9.0425$

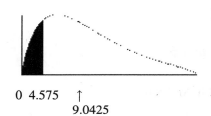

0  4.575    ↑
            9.0425

Do not reject the null hypothesis. There is not enough evidence to support the claim that the standard deviation is less than 15.

## 7.
$H_0$: $\sigma \leq 1.2$    (claim)
$H_1$: $\sigma > 1.2$

$\alpha = 0.01$    d. f. = 14
$\chi^2 = \frac{(n-1)s^2}{\sigma^2} = \frac{(15-1)(1.8)^2}{(1.2)^2} = 31.5$
P-value $< 0.005$    (0.0047)

Since P-value $< 0.01$, reject the null hypothesis. There is enough evidence to reject the claim that the standard deviation is less than or equal to 1.2 minutes.

## 9.
$H_0$: $\sigma \leq 20$
$H_1$: $\sigma > 20$    (claim)

s = 35.11
C. V. = 36.191    $\alpha = 0.01$    d. f. = 19

# Chapter 8 - Hypothesis Testing

## 9. continued

$$\chi^2 = \frac{(n-1)s^2}{\sigma^2} = \frac{(20-1)(35.11)^2}{20^2} = 58.55$$

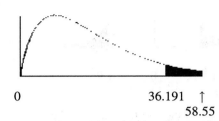

0        36.191   ↑
           58.55

Reject the null hypothesis. There is enough evidence to support the claim that the standard deviation is more than 20 calories.

## 11.

$H_0$: $\sigma \geq 35$
$H_1$: $\sigma < 35$    (claim)

C. V. = 3.940    $\alpha = 0.05$    d. f. = 10
$$\chi^2 = \frac{(n-1)s^2}{\sigma^2} = \frac{(11-1)(32)^2}{35^2} = 8.3592$$

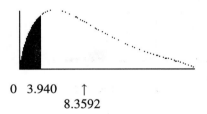

0   3.940     ↑
       8.3592

Do not reject the null hypothesis. There is not enough evidence to support the claim that the standard deviation is less than 35.

## 13.

$H_0$: $\sigma^2 \leq 25$
$H_1$: $\sigma^2 > 25$    (claim)

C. V. = 22.362    $\alpha = 0.05$    d. f. = 13
$$\chi^2 = \frac{(n-1)s^2}{\sigma^2} = \frac{(14-1)(6.74)^2}{25} = 23.622$$

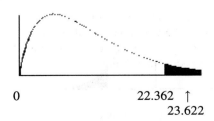

0        22.362   ↑
          23.622

Reject the null hypothesis. There is enough evidence to support the claim that the variance is greater than 25.

## EXERCISE SET 8-7

### 1.

$H_0$: $\mu = 1800$    (claim)
$H_1$: $\mu \neq 1800$

C. V. = ± 1.96
$$z = \frac{\overline{X}-\mu}{\frac{\sigma}{\sqrt{n}}} = \frac{1830-1800}{\frac{200}{\sqrt{10}}} = 0.47$$

− 1.96      0   ↑    1.96
         0.47

The 95% confidence interval of the mean is:
$$\overline{X} - z_{\frac{\alpha}{2}}\frac{\sigma}{\sqrt{n}} < \mu < \overline{X} + z_{\frac{\alpha}{2}}\frac{\sigma}{\sqrt{n}}$$

$$1830 - 1.96\left(\frac{200}{\sqrt{10}}\right) < \mu <$$
$$1830 + 1.96\left(\frac{200}{\sqrt{10}}\right)$$
$$1706.04 < \mu < 1953.96$$

Do not reject. There is not enough evidence to reject the claim that the mean is $1800. The hypothesized mean is within the interval, thus we can be 95% confident that the average sales will be between $1706.94 and $1953.96.

### 3.

$H_0$: $\mu = 86$    (claim)
$H_1$: $\mu \neq 86$

C. V. = ± 2.58
$$z = \frac{\overline{X}-\mu}{\frac{\sigma}{\sqrt{n}}} = \frac{84-86}{\frac{6}{\sqrt{15}}} = -1.29$$

− 2.58   ↑   0      2.58
   − 1.29

$$\overline{X} - z_{\frac{\alpha}{2}}\frac{\sigma}{\sqrt{n}} < \mu < \overline{X} + z_{\frac{\alpha}{2}}\frac{\sigma}{\sqrt{n}}$$

$$84 - 2.58 \cdot \frac{6}{\sqrt{15}} < \mu < 84 + 1.58 \cdot \frac{6}{\sqrt{15}}$$

3. continued

$80.00 < \mu < 88.00$

The decision is do not reject the null hypothesis since $-1.29 > -2.58$ and the 99% confidence interval contains the hypothesized mean. There is not enough evidence to reject the claim that the monthly maintenance is \$86.

5.
$H_0$: $\mu = 22$
$H_1$: $\mu \neq 22$     (claim)

C. V. $= \pm 2.58$
$z = \frac{\overline{X}-\mu}{\frac{\sigma}{\sqrt{n}}} = \frac{20.8-22}{\frac{4}{\sqrt{60}}} = -2.32$

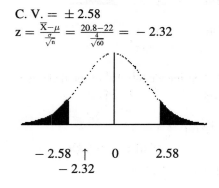

$-2.58 \uparrow \quad 0 \quad 2.58$
$\quad\quad -2.32$

The 99% confidence interval of the mean is:

$$\overline{X} - z_{\frac{\alpha}{2}}\frac{\sigma}{\sqrt{n}} < \mu < \overline{X} + z_{\frac{\alpha}{2}}\frac{\sigma}{\sqrt{n}}$$

$$20.8 - 2.58 \cdot \frac{4}{\sqrt{60}} < \mu < 20.8 + 2.58 \cdot \frac{4}{\sqrt{60}}$$

$19.47 < \mu < 22.13$

The decision is do not reject the null hypothesis since $-2.32 > -2.58$ and the 99% confidence interval does contain the hypothesized mean of 22. The conclusion is that there is not enough evidence to support the claim that the average studying time has changed.

## REVIEW EXERCISES - CHAPTER 8

1.
$H_0$: $\mu = 98°$     (claim)
$H_1$: $\mu \neq 98°$

C. V. $= \pm 1.96$
$z = \frac{\overline{X}-\mu}{\frac{s}{\sqrt{n}}} = \frac{95.8-98}{\frac{7.71}{\sqrt{50}}} = -2.02$

1. continued

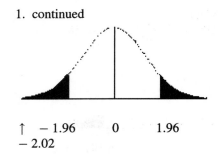

$\uparrow \quad -1.96 \quad\quad 0 \quad\quad 1.96$
$-2.02$

Reject the null hypothesis. There is enough evidence to reject the claim that the average high temperature is 98°.

3.
$H_0$: $\mu \leq \$40,000$
$H_1$: $\mu > \$40,000$     (claim)

C. V. $= 1.65$
$z = \frac{\overline{X}-\mu}{\frac{\sigma}{\sqrt{n}}} = \frac{\$41,000-\$40,000}{\frac{\$3000}{\sqrt{36}}} = 2.00$

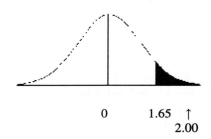

$0 \quad\quad 1.65 \uparrow$
$\quad\quad\quad 2.00$

Reject the null hypothesis. There is enough evidence to support the claim that the average salary is more than \$40,000.

5.
$H_0$: $\mu \leq 67$
$H_1$: $\mu > 67$     (claim)

C. V. $= 1.383$     d. f. $= 9$
$t = \frac{\overline{X}-\mu}{\frac{s}{\sqrt{n}}} = \frac{69.6-67.0}{\frac{1.1}{\sqrt{10}}} = 7.47$

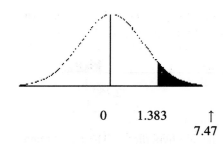

$0 \quad\quad 1.383 \quad\quad \uparrow$
$\quad\quad\quad\quad\quad 7.47$

80

**5. continued**

Reject the null hypothesis. There is enough evidence to support the claim that 1995 was warmer than average.

**7.**

$H_0$: $\mu = 6$
$H_1$: $\mu \neq 6$ (claim)

C. V. $= \pm 2.821$     $\overline{X} = 8.42$     $s = 4.17$

$t = \frac{\overline{X} - \mu}{\frac{s}{\sqrt{n}}} = \frac{8.42 - 6}{\frac{4.17}{\sqrt{10}}} = 1.835$

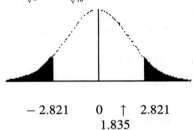

$-2.821$     $0$   $\uparrow$   $2.821$
             $1.835$

Do not reject the null hypothesis. There is not enough evidence to support the claim that the average attendance has changed.

**9.**

$H_0$: $p \leq 0.602$
$H_1$: $p > 0.602$ (claim)

C. V. $= 1.65$
$\hat{p} = 0.65$     $p = 0.602$     $q = 0.398$
$z = \frac{\hat{p} - p}{\sqrt{\frac{pq}{n}}} = \frac{0.65 - 0.602}{\sqrt{\frac{(0.602)(0.398)}{400}}} = 1.96$

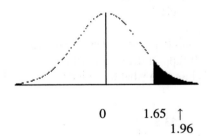

$0$     $1.65$ $\uparrow$
           $1.96$

Reject the null hypothesis. There is enough evidence to support the claim that the percentage of drug offenders is higher than 60.2%.

**11.**

$H_0$: $p = 0.65$ (claim)
$H_1$: $p \neq 0.65$

$\hat{p} = \frac{57}{80} = 0.7125$     $p = 0.65$     $q = 0.35$

**11. continued**

$z = \frac{\hat{p} - p}{\sqrt{\frac{pq}{n}}} = \frac{0.7125 - 0.65}{\sqrt{\frac{(0.65)(0.35)}{80}}} = 1.17$

Area $= 0.3790$
P-value $= 2(0.5 - 0.3790) = 0.242$
Since P-value $> 0.05$, do not reject the null hypothesis. There is not enough evidence to reject the claim that 65% of the teenagers own their own radios.

**13.**

$H_0$: $\mu \geq 10$
$H_1$: $\mu < 10$ (claim)

$z = \frac{\overline{X} - \mu}{\frac{\sigma}{\sqrt{n}}} = \frac{9.25 - 10}{\frac{2}{\sqrt{35}}} = -2.22$

Area $= 0.4868$
P-value $= 0.5 - 0.4699 = 0.0132$
Since $0.0132 < 0.05$, reject the null hypothesis. The conclusion is that there is enough evidence to support the claim that the average time is less than 10 minutes.

**15.**

$H_0$: $\sigma \geq 4.3$ (claim)
$H_1$: $\sigma < 4.3$

d. f. $= 19$
$\chi^2 = \frac{(n-1)s^2}{\sigma^2} = \frac{(20-1)(2.6)^2}{(4.3^2)} = 6.95$

$0.005 <$ P-value $< 0.01$   (0.006)
Since P-value $< 0.05$, reject the null hypothesis. There is enough evidence to reject the claim that the standard deviation is greater than or equal to 4.3 miles per gallon.

**17.**

$H_0$: $\sigma = 18$ (claim)
$H_1$: $\sigma \neq 18$

C. V. $= 11.143$ and $0.484$     d. f. $= 4$

$\chi^2 = \frac{(n-1)s^2}{\sigma^2} = \frac{(5-1)(21)^2}{18^2} = 5.44$

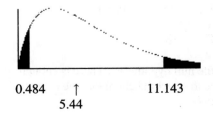

$0.484$     $\uparrow$        $11.143$
           $5.44$

17. continued

Do not reject the null hypothesis. There is not enough evidence to reject the claim that the standard deviation is 18 minutes.

19.
$H_0$: $\mu = 4$
$H_1$: $\mu \neq 4$ (claim)

C. V. $= \pm 2.58$
$z = \frac{\overline{X} - \mu}{\frac{s}{\sqrt{n}}} = \frac{4.2 - 4}{\frac{0.6}{\sqrt{20}}} = 1.49$

The 99% confidence interval of the mean is:

$$\overline{X} - z_{\frac{\alpha}{2}} \frac{\sigma}{\sqrt{n}} < \mu < \overline{X} + z_{\frac{\alpha}{2}} \frac{\sigma}{\sqrt{n}}$$

$4.2 - 2.58 \cdot \frac{0.6}{\sqrt{20}} < \mu < 4.2 + 2.58 \cdot \frac{0.6}{\sqrt{20}}$
$3.85 < \mu < 4.55$

The decision is do not reject the null hypothesis since $1.49 < 2.58$ and the confidence interval does contain the hypothesized mean of 4. There is not enough evidence to support the claim that the growth has changed.

## CHAPTER 8 QUIZ

1. True
2. True
3. False, the critical value separates the critical region from the noncritical region.
4. True
5. False, it can be one-tailed or two-tailed.
6. b
7. d
8. c
9. b
10. Type I
11. $\beta$
12. Statistical hypothesis
13. Right
14. $n - 1$

15. $H_0$: $\mu = 28.6$ (claim)
$H_1$: $\mu \neq 28.6$
C. V. $= \pm 1.96$
$z = 2.14$
Reject the null hypothesis. There is enough evidence to reject the claim that the average age is 28.6.

16. $H_0$: $\mu = \$6,500$ (claim)
$H_1$: $\mu \neq \$6,500$
C. V. $= \pm 1.96$
$z = 5.27$
Reject the null hypothesis. There is enough evidence to reject the agent's claim.

17. $H_0$: $\mu \leq 8$
$H_1$: $\mu > 8$ (claim)
C. V. $= 1.65$
$z = 6.00$
Reject the null hypothesis. There is enough evidence to support the claim that the average number of sticks is greater than 8.

18. $H_0$: $\mu = 500$ (claim)
$H_1$: $\mu \neq 500$
C. V. $= \pm 3.707$
$t = -0.571$
Do not reject the null hypothesis. There is not enough evidence to reject the claim that the average is 500.

19. $H_0$: $\mu \geq 67$
$H_1$: $\mu < 67$ (claim)
$t = -3.1568$
P-value $< 0.005$ (0.003)
Since P-value $< 0.05$, reject the null hypothesis. There is enough evidence to support the claim that the average height is less than 67 inches.

20. $H_0$: $\mu \geq 12.4$
$H_1$: $\mu < 12.4$ (claim)
C. V. $= -1.345$
$t = -2.324$
Reject the null hypothesis. There is enough evidence to support the claim that the average is less than what the company claimed.

21. $H_0$: $\mu \leq 63.5$
$H_1$: $\mu > 63.5$ (claim)
$t = 0.47075$
P-value $> 0.25$ (0.322)
Since P-value $> 0.05$, do not reject the null hypothesis. There is not enough evidence to support the claim that the average is greater than 63.5.

22. $H_0$: $\mu = 26$ (claim)
$H_1$: $\mu \neq 26$
C. V. $= \pm 2.492$
$t = -1.5$

22. continued
Do not reject the null hypothesis. There is not enough evidence to reject the claim that the average age is 26.

23. $H_0$: $p = 0.39$ (claim)
$H_1$: $p \neq 0.39$
C. V. $= \pm 1.96$
$z = -0.62$
Do not reject the null hypothesis. There is not enough evidence to reject the claim that 39% took supplements. The study supports the results of the previous study.

24. $H_0$: $p \geq 0.55$ (claim)
$H_1$: $p < 0.55$
C. V. $= -1.28$
$z = -0.899$
Do not reject the null hypothesis. There is not enough evidence to reject the survey's claim.

25. $H_0$: $p = 0.35$ (claim)
$H_1$: $p \neq 0.35$
C. V. $= \pm 2.33$
$z = 0.666$
Do not reject the null hypothesis. There is not enough evidence to reject the claim that the proportion is 35%.

26. $H_0$: $p = 0.75$ (claim)
$H_1$: $p \neq 0.75$
C. V. $= \pm 2.58$
$z = 2.6833$
Reject the null hypothesis. there is enough evidence to reject the claim.

27. The area corresponding to $z = 2.14$ is 0.4838.
P-value $= 2(0.5 - 0.4838) = 0.0324$

28. The area corresponding to $z = 5.27$ is greater than 0.4999.
Thus, P-value $\leq 2(0.5 - 0.4999) \leq 0.0002$.
(Note: Calculators give 0.0001)

29. $H_0$: $\sigma \leq 6$
$H_1$: $\sigma > 6$ (claim)
C. V. $= 36.415$
$\chi^2 = 54$
Reject the null hypothesis. There is enough evidence to support the claim that the standard deviation is more than 6 pages.

30. $H_0$: $\sigma = 8$ (claim)
$H_1$: $\sigma \neq 8$
C. V. $= 27.991, 79.490$
$\chi^2 = 33.2$
Do not reject the null hypothesis. There is not enough evidence to reject the claim that $\sigma = 8$.

31. $H_0$: $\sigma \geq 2.3$
$H_1$: $\sigma < 2.3$ (claim)
C. V. $= 10.117$
$\chi^2 = 13$
Do not reject the null hypothesis. There is not enough evidence to support the claim that the standard deviation is less than 2.3.

32. $H_0$: $\sigma = 9$ (claim)
$H_1$: $\sigma \neq 9$
$\chi^2 = 13.4$
P-value $> 0.20$ (0.291)
Since P-value $> 0.05$, do not reject the null hypothesis. There is not enough evidence to reject the claim that $\sigma = 9$.

33. $28.9 < \mu < 31.2$; no

34. $\$6562.81 < \mu < \$6,637.19$; no

# Chapter 9 - Testing the Difference Between
## Two Means, Two Variances, and Two Proportions

Note: Graphs are not to scale and are intended to convey a general idea. Answers may vary due to rounding, TI-83's, or computer programs.

**EXERCISE SET 9-2**

**1.**
Testing a single mean involves comparing a sample mean to a specific value such as $\mu = 100$; whereas testing the difference between means means comparing the means of two samples such as $\mu_1 = \mu_2$.

**3.**
The populations must be independent of each other and they must be normally distributed. $s_1$ and $s_2$ can be used in place of $\sigma_1$ and $\sigma_2$ when $\sigma_1$ and $\sigma_2$ are unknown and both samples are each greater than or equal to 30.

**5.**
$H_0$: $\mu_1 = \mu_2$ (claim)
$H_1$: $\mu_1 \neq \mu_2$

C. V. $= \pm 2.58$

$\overline{X}_1 = 662.6111$ $\qquad$ $\overline{X}_2 = 758.875$
$s_1 = 449.8703$ $\qquad$ $s_2 = 474.1258$

$z = \dfrac{(\overline{X}_1 - \overline{X}_2) - (\mu_1 - \mu_2)}{\sqrt{\frac{\sigma_1^2}{n_1} + \frac{\sigma_2^2}{n_2}}} = \dfrac{(662.6111 - 758.875) - 0}{\sqrt{\frac{449.8703^2}{36} + \frac{474.1258^2}{36}}} =$

$z = -0.88$
(TI83 answer is $z = -0.856$)

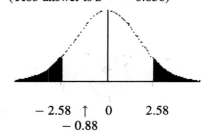

$-2.58 \uparrow \quad 0 \qquad 2.58$
$\quad -0.88$

Do not reject the null hypothesis. There is not enough evidence to reject the claim that the average lengths of the rivers is the same.

**7.**
$H_0$: $\mu_1 \leq \mu_2$
$H_1$: $\mu_1 > \mu_2$ (claim)

C. V. $= 1.65$

**7. continued**
$z = \dfrac{(\overline{X}_1 - \overline{X}_2) - (\mu_1 - \mu_2)}{\sqrt{\frac{s_1^2}{n_1} + \frac{s_2^2}{n_2}}} = \dfrac{(90 - 88) - 0}{\sqrt{\frac{5^2}{100} + \frac{6^2}{100}}} = 2.56$

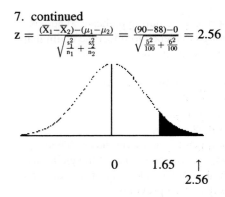

$0 \qquad 1.65 \quad \uparrow$
$\qquad\qquad\qquad 2.56$

Reject the null hypothesis. There is enough evidence to support the claim that pulse rates of smokers are higher than the pulse rates of non-smokers.

**9.**
$H_0$: $\mu_1 \leq \mu_2$
$H_1$: $\mu_1 > \mu_2$ (claim)

C. V. $= 2.05$

$z = \dfrac{(\overline{X}_1 - \overline{X}_2) - (\mu_1 - \mu_2)}{\sqrt{\frac{s_1^2}{n_1} + \frac{s_2^2}{n_2}}} = \dfrac{(61.2 - 59.4) - 0}{\sqrt{\frac{7.9^2}{84} + \frac{7.9^2}{34}}} = 1.12$

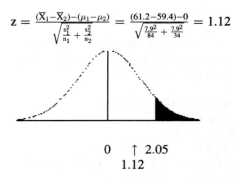

$0 \quad \uparrow 2.05$
$\quad 1.12$

Do not reject the null hypothesis. There is not enough evidence to support the claim that noise levels in the corridors are higher than in the clinics.

**11.**
$H_0$: $\mu_1 \geq \mu_2$
$H_1$: $\mu_1 < \mu_2$ (claim)

C. V. $= -1.65$

$z = \dfrac{(\overline{X}_1 - \overline{X}_2) - (\mu_1 - \mu_2)}{\sqrt{\frac{s_1^2}{n_1} + \frac{s_2^2}{n_2}}} = \dfrac{(3.16 - 3.28) - 0}{\sqrt{\frac{0.52^2}{103} + \frac{0.46^2}{225}}} = -2.01$

**11. continued**

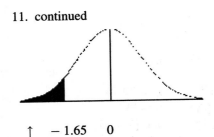

$$\uparrow \quad -1.65 \quad 0$$
$$-2.01$$

Reject the null hypothesis. There is enough evidence to support the claim that stayers have a higher GPA than leavers.

**13.**
$H_0$: $\mu_1 \leq \mu_2$
$H_1$: $\mu_1 > \mu_2$ (claim)

C. V. $= 2.33$
$\overline{X}_1 = \$9224$      $\overline{X}_2 = \$8497.5$
$s_1 = 3829.826$      $s_2 = 2745.293$

$$z = \frac{(\overline{X}_1 - \overline{X}_2) - (\mu_1 - \mu_2)}{\sqrt{\frac{s_1^2}{n_1} + \frac{s_2^2}{n_2}}}$$

$$z = \frac{(9224 - 8497.5) - 0}{\sqrt{\frac{3829.826^2}{50} + \frac{2745.293^2}{50}}} = 1.09$$

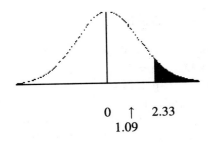

$$0 \quad \uparrow \quad 2.33$$
$$1.09$$

Do not reject the null hypothesis. There is not enough evidence to support the claim that colleges spent more money on men's sports than women's.

**15.**
$H_0$: $\mu_1 = \mu_2$
$H_1$: $\mu_1 \neq \mu_2$ (claim)

$$z = \frac{(\overline{X}_1 - \overline{X}_2) - (\mu_1 - \mu_2)}{\sqrt{\frac{s_1^2}{n_1} + \frac{s_2^2}{n_2}}} = \frac{(3.05 - 2.96) - 0}{\sqrt{\frac{0.75^2}{103} + \frac{0.75^2}{225}}}$$

$z = 1.01$
Area $= 0.3438$
P-value $= 2(0.5 - 0.3438) = 0.3124$

**15. continued**
Do not reject the null hypothesis. There is not enough evidence to support the claim that there is a difference in scores.

**17.**
$\overline{D} = 83.6 - 79.2 = 4.4$
$$(\overline{X}_1 - \overline{X}_2) - z_{\frac{\alpha}{2}}\sqrt{\frac{\sigma_1^2}{n_1} + \frac{\sigma_2^2}{n_2}} < \mu_1 - \mu_2 <$$
$$(\overline{X}_1 - \overline{X}_2) + z_{\frac{\alpha}{2}}\sqrt{\frac{\sigma_1^2}{n_1} + \frac{\sigma_2^2}{n_2}}$$

$$4.4 - (1.65)\sqrt{\frac{4.3^2}{36} + \frac{3.8^2}{36}} < \mu_1 - \mu_2 <$$
$$4.4 + (1.65)\sqrt{\frac{4.3^2}{36} + \frac{3.8^2}{36}}$$

$$2.8 < \mu_1 - \mu_2 < 6.0$$

**19.**
$\overline{D} = 28.6 - 32.9 = -4.3$

$$(\overline{X}_1 - \overline{X}_2) - z_{\frac{\alpha}{2}}\sqrt{\frac{\sigma_1^2}{n_1} + \frac{\sigma_2^2}{n_2}} < \mu_1 - \mu_2 <$$
$$(\overline{X}_1 - \overline{X}_2) + z_{\frac{\alpha}{2}}\sqrt{\frac{\sigma_1^2}{n_1} + \frac{\sigma_2^2}{n_2}}$$

$$-4.3 - (2.58)\sqrt{\frac{5.1^2}{30} + \frac{4.4^2}{40}} < \mu_1 - \mu_2 <$$
$$-4.3 + (2.58)\sqrt{\frac{5.2^2}{30} + \frac{4.4^2}{40}}$$

$$-7.3 < \mu_1 - \mu_2 < -1.3$$

**21.**
$H_0$: $\mu_1 - \mu_2 \leq 8$ (claim)
$H_1$: $\mu_1 - \mu_2 > 8$

C. V. $= 1.65$

$$z = \frac{(\overline{X}_1 - \overline{X}_2) - K}{\sqrt{\frac{s_1^2}{n_1} + \frac{s_2^2}{n_2}}} = \frac{(110 - 104) - 8}{\sqrt{\frac{15^2}{60} + \frac{15^2}{60}}} = -0.73$$

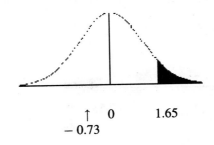

$$\uparrow \quad 0 \quad\quad 1.65$$
$$-0.73$$

Do not reject the null hypothesis. There is not enough evidence to reject the claim that

21. continued
private school students have exam scores
that are at most 8 points higher than public
school students.

EXERCISE SET 9-3

1.
It should be the larger of the two variances.

3.
One d.f. is used for the variance associated
with the numerator and one is used for the
variance associated with the denominator.

5.
a. d. f. N = 15, d. f. D = 22; C. V. = 3.36
b. d. f. N = 24, d. f. D = 13; C. V. = 3.59
c. d. f. N = 45, d. f. D = 29; C. V. = 2.03
d. d. f. N = 20, d. f. D = 16; C. V. = 2.28
e. d. f. N = 10, d. f. D = 10; C. V. = 2.98

6.
Note: Specific P-values are in parentheses.
a. $0.025 < $ P-value $< 0.05$ (0.033)
b. $0.05 < $ P-value $< 0.10$ (0.072)
c. P-value $= 0.05$
d. $0.005 < $ P-value $< 0.01$ (0.006)
e. P-value $= 0.05$
f. $P > 0.10$ (0.112)
g. $0.05 < $ P-value $< 0.10$ (0.068)
h. $0.01 < $ P-value $< 0.02$ (0.015)

7.
$H_0$: $\sigma_1^2 = \sigma_2^2$
$H_1$: $\sigma_1^2 \neq \sigma_2^2$ (claim)

C. V. = 2.53 $\quad \alpha = \frac{0.10}{2}$
d. f. N = 14 $\quad$ d. f. D = 14
$F = \frac{s_1^2}{s_2^2} = \frac{13.12^2}{6.17^2} = 4.52$

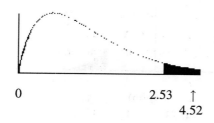

0 $\qquad$ 2.53 $\uparrow$
4.52

Reject the null hypothesis. There is enough
evidence to support the claim that there is a
difference in the variances of the best seller
lists for fiction and non-fiction.

9.
$H_0$: $\sigma_1^2 = \sigma_2^2$

$H_1$: $\sigma_1^2 \neq \sigma_2^2$ (claim)

$s_1 = 25.97 \qquad s_2 = 72.74$
C. V. = 2.86 $\qquad \alpha = \frac{0.05}{2}$
d. f. N = 15 $\qquad$ d. f. D = 15

$F = \frac{s_1^2}{s_2^2} = \frac{72.74^2}{25.97^2} = 7.85$

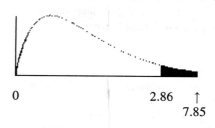

0 $\qquad$ 2.86 $\uparrow$
7.85

Reject the null hypothesis. There is enough
evidence to support the claim that the
variances of the values of tax exempt
properties are different. Since both data sets
vary greatly from normality, the results are
suspect.

11.
$H_0$: $\sigma_1^2 = \sigma_2^2$
$H_1$: $\sigma_1^2 \neq \sigma_2^2$ (claim)

$s_1 = 33.99 \qquad s_2 = 33.99$
C. V. = 4.99 $\qquad \alpha = \frac{0.05}{2}$
d. f. N = 7 $\qquad$ d. f. D = 7
$F = \frac{s_1^2}{s_2^2} = \frac{(33.99)^2}{(33.99)^2} = 1$

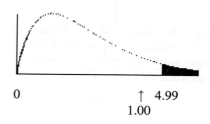

0 $\qquad \uparrow$ 4.99
1.00

Do not reject the null hypothesis. There is
not enough evidence to support the claim
that the variance in the number of calories
differs between the two brands.

13.
$H_0$: $\sigma_1 = \sigma_2$
$H_1$: $\sigma_1 \neq \sigma_2$ (claim)

**13. continued**

$s_1 = 6.8$   $s_2 = 3.2$
$n_1 = 25$   $n_2 = 25$
C. V. = 2.27   $\alpha = \frac{0.05}{2}$
d. f. N = 24   d. f. D = 24
$F = \frac{s_1^2}{s_2^2} = \frac{(6.8)^2}{(3.2)^2} = 4.52$

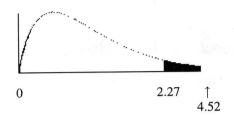

0                    2.27   ↑
                            4.52

Reject the null hypothesis. There is enough evidence to support the claim that the standard deviations are different. One reason is that there are many more people who play the slot machines than people who play roulette. This could possibly account for the larger standard deviation in the ages of the players.

**15.**
$H_0$: $\sigma_1^2 = \sigma_2^2$
$H_1$: $\sigma_1^2 \neq \sigma_2^2$   (claim)

Research: $s_1 = 5501.118$
Primary Care: $s_2 = 5238.809$

C. V. = 4.03   $\alpha = \frac{0.05}{2}$
d. f. N = 9   d. f. D = 9
$F = \frac{s_1^2}{s_2^2} = \frac{(5501.118)^2}{(5238.809)^2} = 1.1026$

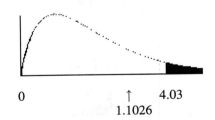

0              ↑        4.03
             1.1026

Do not reject the null hypothesis. There is not enough evidence to support the claim that there is a difference between the variances in tuition costs.

**17.**
$H_0$: $\sigma_1^2 = \sigma_2^2$   (claim)
$H_1$: $\sigma_1^2 \neq \sigma_2^2$

**17. continued**

$s_1 = 130.496$   $s_2 = 73.215$
C. V. = 3.87   $\alpha = \frac{0.10}{2}$
d. f. N = 6   d. f. D = 7
$F = \frac{s_1^2}{s_2^2} = \frac{(130.496)^2}{(73.215)^2} = 3.18$

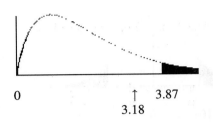

0              ↑    3.87
             3.18

Do not reject the null hypothesis. There is not enough evidence to reject the claim that the variances of the heights are equal.

**19.**

| Men | Women |
|---|---|
| $s_1^2 = 2.363$ | $s_2^2 = 0.444$ |
| $n_1 = 15$ | $n_2 = 15$ |

$H_0$: $\sigma_1^2 = \sigma_2^2$   (claim)
$H_1$: $\sigma_1^2 \neq \sigma_2$

$\alpha = 0.05$        P-value = 0.004
d. f. N = 14   d. f. D = 14
$F = \frac{s_1^2}{s_2^2} = \frac{2.363}{0.444} = 5.32$

Since P-value < 0.01, reject the null hypothesis. There is enough evidence to reject the claim that the variances in weights are equal.

**EXERCISE SET 9-4**

**1.**
$H_0$: $\sigma_1^2 = \sigma_2^2$
$H_1$: $\sigma_1^2 \neq \sigma_2^2$
d. f. N = 9   d. f. D = 9   $\alpha = \frac{0.05}{2}$
$F = \frac{3256^2}{2341^2} = 1.93$   C. V. = 4.03
Do not reject. The variances are equal.

$H_0$: $\mu_1 = \mu_2$
$H_1$: $\mu_1 \neq \mu_2$   (claim)
C. V. = $\pm 2.101$   d. f. = 18

$$t = \frac{(\overline{X}_1 - \overline{X}_2) - (\mu_1 - \mu_2)}{\sqrt{\frac{(n_1-1)s_1^2 + (n_2-1)s_2^2}{n_1+n_2-2}}\sqrt{\frac{1}{n_1}+\frac{1}{n_2}}}$$

**1. continued**

$$t = \frac{(83,256 - 88,354) - 0}{\sqrt{\frac{9(3256)^2 + 9(2341)^2}{18}}\sqrt{\frac{1}{10} + \frac{1}{10}}}$$

$$t = -4.02$$

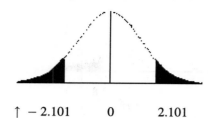

↑ $-2.101$   $0$   $2.101$
$-4.02$

Reject the null hypothesis. There is enough evidence to support the claim that there is a significant difference in the values of the homes based upon the appraisers' values.

Confidence Interval:

$$-5098 - 2.101\left(\sqrt{\frac{9(3256)^2 + 9(2341)^2}{18}}\right.$$

$$\left.\sqrt{\frac{1}{10} + \frac{1}{10}}\right) < \mu_1 - \mu_2 <$$

$$-5098 + 2.101\left(\sqrt{\frac{9(3256)^2 + 9(2341)^2}{18}}\right.$$

$$\left.\sqrt{\frac{1}{10} + \frac{1}{10}}\right) =$$

$$-5098 - 2.101(1268.14) < \mu_1 - \mu_2 <$$
$$-5098 + 2.101(1268.14)$$

$$-\$7762 < \mu_1 - \mu_2 < -\$2434$$

**3.**
$H_0: \sigma_1^2 = \sigma_2^2$
$H_1: \sigma_1^2 \neq \sigma_2^2$

d. f. N = 14    d. f. D = 14    $\alpha = \frac{0.05}{2}$
$F = \frac{20,000^2}{20,000^2} = 1$    C. V. = 3.05
Do not reject. The variances are equal.

$H_0: \mu_1 = \mu_2$
$H_1: \mu_1 \neq \mu_2$    (claim)

C. V. $= \pm 2.048$
d. f. $= 14 + 14 - 2 = 28$

$$t = \frac{(\overline{X}_1 - \overline{X}_2) - (\mu_1 - \mu_2)}{\sqrt{\frac{(n_1 - 1)s_1^2 + (n_2 - 1)s_2^2}{n_1 + n_2 - 2}}\sqrt{\frac{1}{n_1} + \frac{1}{n_2}}}$$

**3. continued**

$$t = \frac{(501,580 - 513,360) - 0}{\sqrt{\frac{14(20,000^2) + 14(20,000^2)}{15 + 15 - 2}}\sqrt{\frac{1}{15} + \frac{1}{15}}}$$

$$t = -1.61$$

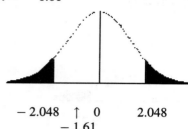

$-2.048$  ↑  $0$   $2.048$
$-1.61$

Do not reject the null hypothesis. There is not enough evidence to reject the claim that there is no difference between the means.

**5.**
$H_0: \sigma_1^2 = \sigma_2^2$
$H_1: \sigma_1^2 \neq \sigma_2^2$
$\overline{X}_1 = 37.167$    $\overline{X}_2 = 25$
$s_1 = 13.2878$    $s_2 = 15.7734$
d. f. N = 5    d. f. D = 5    $\alpha = 0.01$
$F = \frac{15.7734^2}{13.2878^2} = 1.41$    C. V. = 14.94
Do not reject. The variances are equal.

$H_0: \mu_1 \leq \mu_2$
$H_1: \mu_1 > \mu_2$    (claim)

C. V. = 2.764    d. f. = 10
$$t = \frac{(\overline{X}_1 - \overline{X}_2) - (\mu_1 - \mu_2)}{\sqrt{\frac{(n_1 - 1)s_1^2 + (n_2 - 1)s_2^2}{n_1 + n_2 - 2}}\sqrt{\frac{1}{n_1} + \frac{1}{n_2}}}$$

$$t = \frac{(37.167 - 25) - 0}{\sqrt{\frac{5(13.2878)^2 + 5(15.7734)^2}{6 + 6 - 2}}\sqrt{\frac{1}{6} + \frac{1}{6}}} = 1.45$$

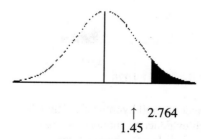

↑ 2.764
1.45

Do not reject the null hypothesis. There is not enough evidence to support the claim that the average number of family day care homes is greater than the average number of day care centers.

**7.**

$H_0$: $\sigma_1^2 = \sigma_2^2$

$H_1$: $\sigma_1^2 \neq \sigma_2^2$

d. f. N = 9    d. f. D = 13    $\alpha = 0.02$

$F = \frac{5.6^2}{4.3^2} = 1.7$    C. V. = 4.19

Do not reject. The variances are equal.

$H_0$: $\mu_1 = \mu_2$

$H_1$: $\mu_1 \neq \mu_2$    (claim)

C. V. = $\pm 2.508$    d. f. = 22

$$t = \frac{(\overline{X}_1 - \overline{X}_2) - (\mu_1 - \mu_2)}{\sqrt{\frac{(n_1-1)s_1^2 + (n_2-1)s_2^2}{n_1 + n_2 - 2}}\sqrt{\frac{1}{n_1} + \frac{1}{n_2}}}$$

$$t = \frac{(21 - 27) - 0}{\sqrt{\frac{9(5.6)^2 + 13(4.3)^2}{10 + 14 - 2}}\sqrt{\frac{1}{10} + \frac{1}{14}}} = -2.97$$

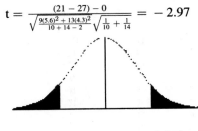

↑ − 2.508     0     2.508

− 2.97

Reject the null hypothesis. There is enough evidence to support the claim that there is a difference in the average times of the two groups.

Confidence Interval:

$-6 - 2.508(2.02) < \mu_1 - \mu_2 <$

$\qquad\qquad -6 + 2.508(2.02)$

$-11.1 < \mu_1 - \mu_2 < -0.93$

**9.**

$H_0$: $\sigma_1^2 = \sigma_2^2$

$H_1$: $\sigma_1^2 \neq \sigma_2^2$

d. f. N = 24    d. f. D = 24    $\alpha = 0.10$

$F = \frac{3.20^2}{2.57^2} = 1.55$    C.V. = 1.98

Do not reject. The variances are equal.

$H_0$: $\mu_1 \leq \mu_2$

$H_1$: $\mu_1 > \mu_2$    (claim)

C.V. = 1.282    df = 48

$$t = \frac{(\overline{X}_1 - \overline{X}_2) - (\mu_1 - \mu_2)}{\sqrt{\frac{(n_1-1)s_1^2 + (n_2-1)s_2^2}{n_1 + n_2 - 2}}\sqrt{\frac{1}{n_1} + \frac{1}{n_2}}}$$

$$t = \frac{(19.63 - 10.25) - 0}{\sqrt{\frac{24(3.2)^2 + 24(2.57)^2}{25 + 25 - 2}}\sqrt{\frac{1}{25} + \frac{1}{25}}}$$

t = 11.427

**9. continued**

Reject the null hypothesis. There is enough evidence to support the claim that the average cost of a movie ticket in London is greater than the average cost of a ticket in New York City. One reason for the difference could be the rate of exchange of the money.

**11.**

| White Mice | Brown Mice |
|---|---|
| $\overline{X}_1 = 17$ | $\overline{X}_2 = 16.67$ |
| $s_1 = 4.56$ | $s_2 = 5.05$ |
| $n_1 = 6$ | $n_2 = 6$ |

$H_0$: $\sigma_1^2 = \sigma_2^2$

$H_1$: $\sigma_1^2 \neq \sigma_2^2$

d. f. N = 5    d. f. D = 5    $\alpha = \frac{0.05}{2}$

$F = \frac{5.05^2}{4.56^2} = 1.23$    C. V. = 7.15

Do not reject. The variances are equal.

$H_0$: $\mu_1 = \mu_2$

$H_1$: $\mu_1 \neq \mu_2$    (claim)

C. V. = $\pm 2.228$    d. f. = 10

$$t = \frac{(17 - 16.67) - 0}{\sqrt{\frac{5(4.56)^2 + 5(5.05)^2}{6 + 6 - 2}}\sqrt{\frac{1}{6} + \frac{1}{6}}} = 0.119$$

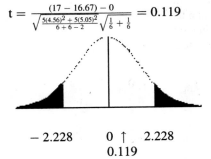

− 2.228     0 ↑    2.228

0.119

Do not reject the null hypothesis. There is not enough evidence to support the claim that the color of the mice made a difference.

Confidence Interval:

$0.33 - 2.228(2.78) < \mu_1 - \mu_2 <$

$\qquad\qquad 0.33 + 2.228(2.78)$

$-5.9 < \mu_1 - \mu_2 < 6.5$

**13.**

Private: $\overline{X} = \$16,147.5$    s = 4023.7

Public: $\overline{X} = \$9039.9$    s = 3325.5

F test:

d. f. N = 6 − 1 = 5

d. f. D = 7 − 1 = 6

13. continued

C. V. = 5.99

$F = \frac{4023.7^2}{3325.5^2} = 1.46$

Do not reject. The variances are equal.

Confidence Interval:

$$t_{\frac{\alpha}{2}} \sqrt{\frac{(n_1-1)s_1^2 + (n_2-1)s_2^2}{n_1+n_2-2}} \sqrt{\frac{1}{n_1} + \frac{1}{n_2}} =$$

$$2.201 \sqrt{\frac{5(4023.7)^2 + 6(3325.5)^2}{6+7-2}} \sqrt{\frac{1}{6} + \frac{1}{7}}$$

$= 4481.04$

$16,147.5 - 9039.9 = 7107.6$

$7107.6 - 4481.04 < \mu_1 - \mu_2 <$
$\qquad 7107.6 + 4481.04$

$\$2626.60 < \mu_1 - \mu_2 < \$11,588.64$

## EXERCISE SET 9-5

1.
a. Dependent
b. Dependent
c. Independent
d. Dependent
e. Independent

3.

| Before | After | D | D$^2$ |
|--------|-------|----|-----|
| 9 | 9 | 0 | 0 |
| 12 | 17 | -5 | 25 |
| 6 | 9 | -3 | 9 |
| 15 | 20 | -5 | 25 |
| 3 | 2 | 1 | 1 |
| 18 | 21 | -3 | 9 |
| 10 | 15 | -5 | 25 |
| 13 | 22 | -9 | 81 |
| 7 | 6 | 1 | 1 |

$\sum D = -28 \quad \sum D^2 = 176$

$H_0$: $\mu_D \geq 0$
$H_1$: $\mu_D < 0$ (claim)

C. V. = $-1.397$     d. f. = 8

$\overline{D} = \frac{\sum D}{n} = -3.11$

$s_D = \sqrt{\frac{\sum D^2 - \frac{(\sum D)^2}{n}}{n-1}} = \sqrt{\frac{176 - \frac{(-28)^2}{9}}{8}} = 3.33$

$t = \frac{-3.11 - 0}{\frac{3.33}{\sqrt{9}}} = -2.8$

3. continued

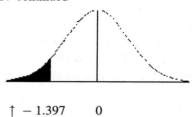

↑ $-1.397$     0
$-2.8$

Reject the null hypothesis. There is enough evidence to support the claim that the seminar increased the number of hours students studied.

5.

| F - S | S - Th | D | D$^2$ |
|-------|--------|----|-----|
| 4 | 8 | -4 | 16 |
| 7 | 5.5 | 1.5 | 2.25 |
| 10.5 | 7.5 | 3 | 9 |
| 12 | 8 | 4 | 16 |
| 11 | 7 | 4 | 16 |
| 9 | 6 | 3 | 9 |
| 6 | 6 | 0 | 0 |
| 9 | 8 | 1 | 1 |

$\sum D = 12.5 \quad \sum D^2 = 69.25$

$H_0$: $\mu_D = 0$
$H_1$: $\mu_D \neq 0$ (claim)

C. V. = $\pm 2.365$      d. f. = 7

$\overline{D} = \frac{\sum D}{n} = \frac{12.5}{8} = 1.5625$

$s_D = \sqrt{\frac{\sum D^2 - \frac{(\sum D)^2}{n}}{n-1}}$

$= \sqrt{\frac{69.25 - \frac{(12.5)^2}{8}}{7}} = 2.665$

$t = \frac{1.5625 - 0}{\frac{2.665}{\sqrt{8}}} = 1.6583$

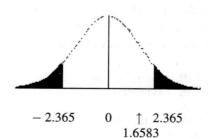

$-2.365$     0   ↑ 2.365
$\qquad\qquad$ 1.6583

Do not reject the null hypothesis. There is not enough evidence to support the claim that there is a difference in the mean number of hours slept.

**7.**

| Before | After | D | $D^2$ |
|--------|-------|-----|-----|
| 12 | 9 | 3 | 9 |
| 9 | 6 | 3 | 9 |
| 0 | 1 | -1 | 1 |
| 5 | 3 | 2 | 4 |
| 4 | 2 | 2 | 4 |
| 3 | 3 | 0 | 0 |
| | | $\sum D = 9$ | $\sum D^2 = 27$ |

$H_0$: $\mu_D \leq 0$

$H_1$: $\mu_D > 0$  (claim)

C. V. = 2.571     d. f. = 5

$\overline{D} = \frac{\sum D}{n} = \frac{9}{6} = 1.5$

$s_D = \sqrt{\frac{\sum D^2 - \frac{(\sum D)^2}{n}}{n-1}} = \sqrt{\frac{27 - \frac{9^2}{6}}{5}} = 1.64$

$t = \frac{1.5 - 0}{\frac{1.64}{\sqrt{6}}} = 2.24$

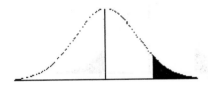

0   ↑   2.571
   2.24

Do not reject the null hypothesis. There is not enough evidence to support the claim that the errors have been reduced.

**9.**

| A | B | D | $D^2$ |
|-----|-----|-----|-----|
| 87 | 83 | 4 | 16 |
| 92 | 95 | -3 | 9 |
| 78 | 79 | -1 | 1 |
| 83 | 83 | 0 | 0 |
| 88 | 86 | 2 | 4 |
| 90 | 93 | -3 | 9 |
| 84 | 80 | 4 | 16 |
| 93 | 86 | 7 | 49 |
| | | $\sum D = 10$ | $\sum D^2 = 104$ |

$H_0$: $\mu_D = 0$

$H_1$: $\mu_D \neq 0$  (claim)

d. f. = 7

$\overline{D} = \frac{\sum D}{n} = \frac{10}{8} = 1.25$

**9. continued**

$s_D = \sqrt{\frac{\sum D^2 - \frac{(\sum D)^2}{n}}{n-1}} = \sqrt{\frac{104 - \frac{10^2}{8}}{7}} = 3.62$

$t = \frac{1.25 - 0}{\frac{3.62}{\sqrt{8}}} = 0.978$

0.20 < P-value < 0.50 (0.361)  Do not reject the null hypothesis since P-value > 0.01. There is not enough evidence to support the claim that there is a difference in the pulse rates.

Confidence Interval:

$1.25 - 3.499\left(\frac{3.62}{\sqrt{8}}\right) < \mu_D <$
$\qquad 1.25 + 3.499\left(\frac{3.62}{\sqrt{8}}\right)$

$-3.23 < \mu_D < 5.73$

**11.**

Using the previous problem, $\overline{D} = -1.5625$ whereas the mean of the 1994 values is 95.375 and the mean of the 1999 values is 96.9375; hence,

$\overline{D} = 95.375 - 96.9375 = -1.5625$

## EXERCISE SET 9-6

**1A.**

Use $\hat{p} = \frac{X}{n}$ and $\hat{q} = 1 - \hat{p}$

a. $\hat{p} = \frac{34}{48}$      $\hat{q} = \frac{14}{48}$

b. $\hat{p} = \frac{28}{75}$      $\hat{q} = \frac{47}{75}$

c. $\hat{p} = \frac{50}{100}$      $\hat{q} = \frac{50}{100}$

d. $\hat{p} = \frac{6}{24}$      $\hat{q} = \frac{18}{24}$

e. $\hat{p} = \frac{12}{144}$      $\hat{q} = \frac{132}{144}$

**1B.**

a. x = 0.16(100) = 16
b. x = 0.08(50) = 4
c. x = 0.06(800) = 48
d. x = 0.52(200) = 104
e. x = 0.20(150) = 30

**3.**

$\hat{p}_1 = \frac{X_1}{n_1} = \frac{80}{150} = 0.533$   $\hat{p}_2 = \frac{30}{100} = 0.3$

$\overline{p} = \frac{X_1 + X_2}{n_1 + n_2} = \frac{80 + 30}{150 + 100} = \frac{110}{250} = 0.44$

3. continued
$\bar{q} = 1 - \bar{p} = 1 - 0.44 = 0.56$

$H_0$: $p_1 = p_2$
$H_1$: $p_1 \neq p_2$    (claim)

C. V. $= \pm 1.96$

$z = \dfrac{(\hat{p}_1 - \hat{p}_2) - (p_1 - p_2)}{\sqrt{(\bar{p})(\bar{q})\left(\frac{1}{n_1} + \frac{1}{n_2}\right)}} = \dfrac{(0.533 - 0.3) - 0}{\sqrt{(0.44)(0.56)\left(\frac{1}{150} + \frac{1}{100}\right)}}$

$z = 3.64$

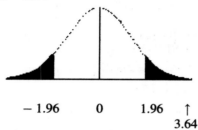

$-1.96 \qquad 0 \qquad 1.96 \quad \uparrow$
$\qquad\qquad\qquad\qquad\qquad 3.64$

**Reject the null hypothesis. There is enough evidence to support the claim that there is a significant difference in the proportions.**

5.
$\hat{p}_1 = \dfrac{X_1}{n_1} = \dfrac{112}{150} = 0.7467 \qquad \hat{p}_2 = \dfrac{150}{200} = 0.75$

$\bar{p} = \dfrac{X_1 + X_2}{n_1 + n_2} = \dfrac{112 + 150}{150 + 200} = 0.749$

$\bar{q} = 1 - \bar{p} = 1 - 0.749 = 0.251$

$H_0$: $p_1 = p_2$
$H_1$: $p_1 \neq p_2$    (claim)

C. V. $= \pm 1.96$

$z = \dfrac{(\hat{p}_1 - \hat{p}_2) - (p_1 - p_2)}{\sqrt{(\bar{p})(\bar{q})\left(\frac{1}{n_1} + \frac{1}{n_2}\right)}} = \dfrac{(0.7467 - 0.75) - 0}{\sqrt{(0.749)(0.251)\left(\frac{1}{150} + \frac{1}{200}\right)}}$

$z = -0.07$

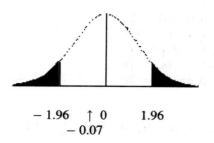

$-1.96 \quad \uparrow 0 \qquad 1.96$
$\qquad -0.07$

5. continued
Do not reject the null hypothesis. There is not enough evidence to support the claim that the proportions are different.

7.
$\hat{p}_1 = 0.83 \qquad \hat{p}_2 = 0.75$
$X_1 = 0.83(100) = 83$
$X_2 = 0.75(100) = 75$

$\bar{p} = \dfrac{83 + 75}{100 + 100} = 0.79 \qquad \bar{q} = 1 - 0.79 = 0.21$

$H_0$: $p_1 = p_2$    (claim)
$H_1$: $p_1 \neq p_2$
C. V. $= \pm 1.96 \qquad \alpha = 0.05$

$z = \dfrac{(\hat{p}_1 - \hat{p}_2) - (p_1 - p_2)}{\sqrt{(\bar{p})(\bar{q})\left(\frac{1}{n_1} + \frac{1}{n_2}\right)}} = \dfrac{(0.83 - 0.75) - 0}{\sqrt{(0.79)(0.21)\left(\frac{1}{100} + \frac{1}{100}\right)}}$

$z = 1.39$

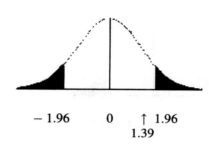

$-1.96 \qquad 0 \quad \uparrow 1.96$
$\qquad\qquad\qquad 1.39$

Do not reject the null hypothesis. There is not enough evidence to reject the claim that the proportions are equal.

$(\hat{p}_1 - \hat{p}_2) - z_{\frac{\alpha}{2}} \sqrt{\dfrac{\hat{p}_1\hat{q}_1}{n_1} + \dfrac{\hat{p}_2\hat{q}_2}{n_2}} < p_1 - p_2 <$

$\qquad (\hat{p}_1 - \hat{p}_2) + z_{\frac{\alpha}{2}} \sqrt{\dfrac{\hat{p}_1\hat{q}_1}{n_1} + \dfrac{\hat{p}_2\hat{q}_2}{n_2}}$

$0.08 - 1.96 \sqrt{\dfrac{0.83(0.17)}{100} + \dfrac{0.75(0.25)}{100}} < p_1 - p_2$

$\qquad < 0.08 + 1.96 \sqrt{\dfrac{0.83(0.17)}{100} + \dfrac{0.75(0.25)}{100}}$

$-0.032 < p_1 - p_2 < 0.192$

9.
$\hat{p}_1 = 0.55 \qquad \hat{p}_2 = 0.45$

$X_1 = 0.55(80) = 44 \quad X_2 = 0.45(90) = 40.5$

$\bar{p} = \dfrac{X_1 + X_2}{n_1 + n_2} = \dfrac{44 + 40.5}{80 + 90} = 0.497$

9. continued

$\bar{q} = 1 - \bar{p} = 1 - 0.497 = 0.503$

$H_0$: $p_1 = p_2$
$H_1$: $p_1 \neq p_2$   (claim)

C. V. $= \pm 2.58$   $\alpha = 0.01$

$z = \dfrac{(\hat{p}_1 - \hat{p}_2) - (p_1 - p_2)}{\sqrt{(\bar{p})(\bar{q})(\frac{1}{n_1} + \frac{1}{n_2})}} = \dfrac{(0.55-0.45)-0}{\sqrt{(0.497)(0.503)(\frac{1}{80}+\frac{1}{90})}}$

$z = 1.302$

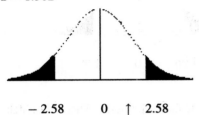

$-2.58$     $0$  $\uparrow$  $2.58$
                $1.302$

Do not reject the null hypothesis. There is not enough evidence to support the claim that the proportions are different.

$(\hat{p}_1 - \hat{p}_2) - z_{\frac{\alpha}{2}} \sqrt{\frac{\hat{p}_1\hat{q}_1}{n_1} + \frac{\hat{p}_2\hat{q}_2}{n_2}} < p_1 - p_2 <$

$(\hat{p}_1 - \hat{p}_2) + z_{\frac{\alpha}{2}} \sqrt{\frac{\hat{p}_1\hat{q}_1}{n_1} + \frac{\hat{p}_2\hat{q}_2}{n_2}}$

$0.1 - 2.58\sqrt{\frac{0.55(0.45)}{80} + \frac{0.45(0.55)}{90}} < p_1 - p_2$

$< 0.1 + 2.58\sqrt{\frac{0.55(0.45)}{80} + \frac{0.45(0.55)}{90}}$

$-0.097 < p_1 - p_2 < 0.297$

11.
$\hat{p}_1 = \frac{26}{75} = 0.3467$     $\hat{p}_2 = \frac{26}{60} = 0.4333$

$\bar{p} = \frac{X_1 + X_2}{n_1 + n_2} = \frac{26 + 26}{75 + 60} = 0.3852$

$\bar{q} = 1 - \bar{p} = 1 - 0.3852 = 0.6148$

$H_0$: $p_1 = p_2$
$H_1$: $p_1 \neq p_2$   (claim)

C. V. $= \pm 1.96$   $\alpha = 0.05$

$z = \dfrac{(\hat{p}_1 - \hat{p}_2) - (p_1 - p_2)}{\sqrt{(\bar{p})(\bar{q})(\frac{1}{n_1} + \frac{1}{n_2})}} = \dfrac{(0.3467-0.4333)-0}{\sqrt{(0.3852)(0.6148)(\frac{1}{75}+\frac{1}{60})}}$

$z = -1.027$ or $-1.03$

11. continued

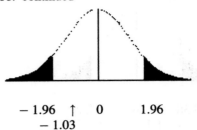

$-1.96$  $\uparrow$  $0$     $1.96$
   $-1.03$

Do not reject the null hypothesis. There is not enough evidence to support the claim that the proportin of dog owners has changed.

$(\hat{p}_1 - \hat{p}_2) - z_{\frac{\alpha}{2}} \sqrt{\frac{\hat{p}_1\hat{q}_1}{n_1} + \frac{\hat{p}_2\hat{q}_2}{n_2}} < p_1 - p_2 <$

$(\hat{p}_1 - \hat{p}_2) + z_{\frac{\alpha}{2}} \sqrt{\frac{\hat{p}_1\hat{q}_1}{n_1} + \frac{\hat{p}_2\hat{q}_2}{n_2}}$

$-0.0866 - 1.96\sqrt{\frac{0.3467(0.6533)}{75} + \frac{0.4333(0.5667)}{60}}$
$< p_1 - p_2 <$

$-0.0866 + 1.96\sqrt{\frac{0.3467(0.6533)}{75} + \frac{0.4333(0.5667)}{60}}$

$-0.252 < p_1 - p_2 < 0.079$

Yes, the confidence interval contains 0. This is another way to conclude that there is no difference in the proportions.

13.
$\hat{p}_1 = \frac{X_1}{n_1} = \frac{50}{200} = 0.25$

$\hat{p}_2 = \frac{X_2}{n_2} = \frac{93}{300} = 0.31$

$\bar{p} = \frac{X_1 + X_2}{n_1 + n_2} = \frac{50 + 93}{200 + 300} = 0.286$

$\bar{q} = 1 - \bar{p} = 1 - 0.286 = 0.714$

$H_0$: $p_1 = p_2$
$H_1$: $p_1 \neq p_2$   (claim)

C. V. $= \pm 2.58$   $\alpha = 0.01$

$z = \dfrac{(\hat{p}_1 - \hat{p}_2) - (p_1 - p_2)}{\sqrt{(\bar{p})(\bar{q})(\frac{1}{n_1} + \frac{1}{n_2})}} = \dfrac{(0.25-0.31)-0}{\sqrt{(0.286)(0.714)(\frac{1}{200}+\frac{1}{300})}}$

$z = -1.45$

**13. continued**

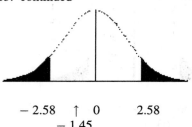

$$-2.58 \quad \uparrow \quad 0 \qquad 2.58$$
$$-1.45$$

Do not reject the null hypothesis. There is not enough evidence to support the claim that the proportions are different.

$$(\hat{p}_1 - \hat{p}_2) - z_{\frac{\alpha}{2}}\sqrt{\frac{\hat{p}_1\hat{q}_1}{n_1} + \frac{\hat{p}_2\hat{q}_2}{n_2}} < p_1 - p_2 <$$

$$(\hat{p}_1 - \hat{p}_2) + z_{\frac{\alpha}{2}}\sqrt{\frac{\hat{p}_1\hat{q}_1}{n_1} + \frac{\hat{p}_2\hat{q}_2}{n_2}}$$

$$-0.06 - 2.58\sqrt{\frac{0.25(0.75)}{200} + \frac{0.31(0.69)}{300}} <$$

$$p_1 - p_2 < -0.06 + 2.58\sqrt{\frac{0.25(0.75)}{200} + \frac{0.31(0.69)}{300}}$$

$$-0.165 < p_1 - p_2 < 0.045$$

**15.**
$$\alpha = 0.01$$
$$\hat{p}_1 = 0.8 \qquad \hat{q}_1 = 0.2$$
$$\hat{p}_2 = 0.6 \qquad \hat{q}_2 = 0.4$$

$$\hat{p}_1 - \hat{p}_2 = 0.8 - 0.6 = 0.2$$

$$(\hat{p}_1 - \hat{p}_2) - z_{\frac{\alpha}{2}}\sqrt{\frac{\hat{p}_1\hat{q}_1}{n_1} + \frac{\hat{p}_2\hat{q}_2}{n_2}} < p_1 - p_2 <$$

$$(\hat{p}_1 - \hat{p}_2) + z_{\frac{\alpha}{2}}\sqrt{\frac{\hat{p}_1\hat{q}_1}{n_1} + \frac{\hat{p}_2\hat{q}_2}{n_2}}$$

$$0.2 - 2.58\sqrt{\frac{(0.8)(0.2)}{150} + \frac{(0.6)(0.4)}{200}} < p_1 - p_2 <$$

$$0.2 + 2.58\sqrt{\frac{(0.8)(0.2)}{150} + \frac{(0.6)(0.4)}{200}}$$

$$0.077 < p_1 - p_2 < 0.323$$

**17.**
$$\hat{p}_1 = \frac{X_1}{n_1} = \frac{43}{100} = 0.43 \quad \hat{p}_2 = \frac{58}{100} = 0.58$$

$$\bar{p} = \frac{X_1 + X_2}{n_1 + n_2} = \frac{43 + 58}{100 + 100} = 0.505$$

$$\bar{q} = 1 - \bar{p} = 1 - 0.505 = 0.495$$

**17. continued**
$$H_0: \; p_1 = p_2$$
$$H_1: \; p_1 \neq p_2 \quad \text{(claim)}$$

$$\text{C. V.} = \pm 1.96$$

$$z = \frac{(\hat{p}_1 - \hat{p}_2) - (p_1 - p_2)}{\sqrt{(\bar{p})(\bar{q})\left(\frac{1}{n_1} + \frac{1}{n_2}\right)}} = \frac{(0.43 - 0.58) - 0}{\sqrt{(0.505)(0.495)(\frac{1}{100} + \frac{1}{100})}}$$

$$z = -2.12$$

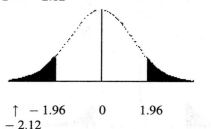

$$\uparrow \; -1.96 \qquad 0 \qquad 1.96$$
$$-2.12$$

Reject the null hypothesis. There is enough evidence to support the claim that the proportions are different.

**19.**
$$\hat{p}_1 = 0.2875 \qquad \hat{q}_1 = 0.7125$$
$$\hat{p}_2 = 0.2857 \qquad \hat{q}_2 = 0.7143$$

$$\hat{p}_1 - \hat{p}_2 = 0.0018$$

$$(\hat{p}_1 - \hat{p}_2) - z_{\frac{\alpha}{2}}\sqrt{\frac{\hat{p}_1\hat{q}_1}{n_1} + \frac{\hat{p}_2\hat{q}_2}{n_2}} < p_1 - p_2 <$$

$$(\hat{p}_1 - \hat{p}_2) + z_{\frac{\alpha}{2}}\sqrt{\frac{\hat{p}_1\hat{q}_1}{n_1} + \frac{\hat{p}_2\hat{q}_2}{n_2}}$$

$$0.0018 - 1.96\sqrt{\frac{(0.2875)(0.7125)}{400} + \frac{(0.2857)(0.7143)}{350}} < p_1 - p_2$$

$$< 0.0018 + 1.96\sqrt{\frac{(0.2875)(0.7125)}{400} + \frac{(0.2857)(0.7143)}{350}}$$

$$-0.0631 < p_1 - p_2 < 0.0667$$

It does agree with the *Almanac* statistics stating a difference of $-0.042$ since $-0.042$ is contained in the interval.

**REVIEW EXERCISES - CHAPTER 9**

**1.**
$$H_0: \; \mu_1 \leq \mu_2$$
$$H_1: \; \mu_1 > \mu_2 \quad \text{(claim)}$$

$$\text{CV} = 2.33 \qquad \alpha = 0.01$$
$$\bar{X}_1 = 120.1 \qquad \bar{X}_2 = 117.8$$
$$s_1 = 16.722 \qquad s_2 = 16.053$$

# Chapter 9 - Testing the Difference Between
## Two Means, Two Variances, and Two Proportions

**1. continued**

$$z = \frac{(\overline{X}_1 - \overline{X}_2) - (\mu_1 - \mu_2)}{\sqrt{\frac{s_1^2}{n_1} + \frac{s_2^2}{n_2}}} = \frac{(120.1 - 117.8) - 0}{\sqrt{\frac{16.722^2}{36} + \frac{16.053^2}{35}}}$$

$z = 0.587$ or $0.59$

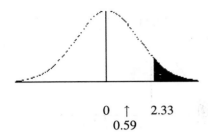

$$0 \quad \uparrow \quad 2.33$$
$$0.59$$

Do not reject the null hypothesis. There is not enough evidence to support the claim that single people do more pleasure driving than married people.

**3.**

$H_0$: $\sigma_1 = \sigma_2$
$H_1$: $\sigma_1 \neq \sigma_2$  (claim)

C. V. $= 2.77$    $\alpha = 0.10$
d. f. N $= 23$    d. f. D $= 10$

$$F = \frac{13.2^2}{4.1^2} = 10.365$$

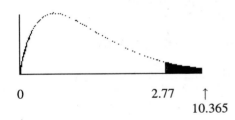

$$0 \qquad\qquad 2.77 \quad \uparrow$$
$$10.365$$

Reject the null hypothesis. There is enough evidence to support the claim that there is a difference in standard deviations.

**5.**

$H_0$: $\sigma_1^2 \leq \sigma_2^2$
$H_1$: $\sigma_1^2 > \sigma_2^2$  (claim)

$\alpha = 0.05$
d. f. N $= 9$        d. f. D $= 9$
$$F = \frac{s_1^2}{s_2^2} = \frac{6.3^2}{2.8^2} = 5.06$$

The P-value for the F test is
$0.01 < P\text{-value} < 0.025$  $(0.012)$. Since P-value $< 0.05$, reject the null hypothesis.

**5. continued**

There is enough evidence to support the claim that the variance of the number of speeding tickets on Route 19 is greater than the variance of the number of speeding tickets issued on Route 22.

**7.**

$H_0$: $\sigma_1^2 \leq \sigma_2^2$
$H_1$: $\sigma_1^2 > \sigma_2^2$  (claim)

C. V. $= 1.47$        $\alpha = 0.10$
d. f. N $= 64$        d. f. D $= 41$

$$F = \frac{s_1^2}{s_2^2} = \frac{3.2^2}{2.1^2} = 2.32$$

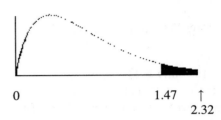

$$0 \qquad\qquad 1.47 \quad \uparrow$$
$$2.32$$

Reject the null hypothesis. There is enough evidence to support the claim that the variation in the number of days factory workers miss per year due to illness is greater than the variation in the number of days hospital workers miss per year.

**9.**

$H_0$: $\sigma_1^2 = \sigma_2^2$
$H_1$: $\sigma_1^2 \neq \sigma_2^2$

$\overline{X}_1 = 72.9$        $\overline{X}_2 = 70.8$
$s_1 = 5.5$            $s_2 = 5.8$
CV $= 1.98$          $\alpha = 0.01$
dfN $= 24$            dfD $= 24$
$F = \frac{5.8^2}{5.5^2} = 1.11$

Do not reject $H_0$. The variances are equal.

$H_0$: $\mu_1 \leq \mu_2$
$H_1$: $\mu_1 > \mu_2$  (claim)

C. V. $= 1.28$    d. f. $= 48$    $\alpha = 0.10$

$$t = \frac{(\overline{X}_1 - \overline{X}_2) - (\mu_1 - \mu_2)}{\sqrt{\frac{(n_1 - 1)s_1^2 + (n_2 - 1)s_2^2}{n_1 + n_2 - 2}} \sqrt{\frac{1}{n_1} + \frac{1}{n_2}}}$$

$$t = \frac{(72.9 - 70.8) - 0}{\sqrt{\frac{24(5.5)^2 + 24(5.8)^2}{25 + 25 - 2}} \sqrt{\frac{1}{25} + \frac{1}{25}}} = 1.31$$

**9. continued**

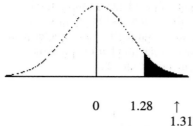

0      1.28     ↑
                1.31

Reject the null hypothesis. There is enough evidence to support the claim that it is warmer in Birmingham.

**11.**

$H_0$: $\sigma_1^2 = \sigma_2^2$
$H_1$: $\sigma_1^2 \neq \sigma_2^2$
$\overline{X}_1 = 150.8333$    $s_1 = 173.1432$
$\overline{X}_2 = 254$    $s_2 = 183.4748$
$\alpha = 0.05$
dfN = 15    dfD = 11
$F = \frac{183.47^2}{173.14^2} = 1.12$  (TI83 gives 0.89)
Do not reject $H_0$ since P-value > 0.10. The variances are equal.

$H_0$: $\mu_1 = \mu_2$
$H_1$: $\mu_1 \neq \mu_2$    (claim)

$\alpha = 0.05$    P-value = 0.4348

$t = \dfrac{(150.8333 - 254) - 0}{\sqrt{\frac{5(173.1432)^2 + 2(183.4748)^2}{7}} \sqrt{\frac{1}{6} + \frac{1}{3}}} = -0.828$

Do not reject the null hypothesis since P-value > 0.10. There is not enough evidence to support the claim that the means are different. A cafeteria manager would want to know the results in order to make a decision on which beverage to serve.

**13.**

| Before | After | D | $D^2$ |
|--------|-------|-----|------|
| 6 | 10 | -4 | 16 |
| 8 | 12 | -4 | 16 |
| 10 | 9 | 1 | 1 |
| 9 | 12 | -3 | 9 |
| 5 | 8 | -3 | 9 |
| 12 | 13 | -1 | 1 |
| 9 | 8 | 1 | 1 |
| 7 | 10 | -3 | 9 |

$\sum D = -16$    $\sum D^2 = 62$

$H_0$: $\mu_D \geq 0$
$H_1$: $\mu_D < 0$    (claim)

**13. continued**
C. V. $= -1.895$    d. f. $= 7$    $\alpha = 0.05$

$\overline{D} = \frac{\sum D}{n} = \frac{-16}{8} = -2$
$s_D = \sqrt{\frac{62 - \frac{(-16)^2}{8}}{7}} = 2.07$

$t = \frac{-2 - 0}{\frac{2.07}{\sqrt{8}}} = -2.73$

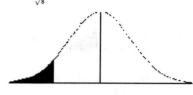

↑   $-1.895$      0
$-2.73$

Reject the null hypothesis. There is enough evidence to support the claim that the music has increased production.

**15.**
$\hat{p}_1 = \frac{18}{120} = 0.15$        $\hat{p}_2 = \frac{5}{100} = 0.05$

$\overline{p} = \frac{18 + 5}{120 + 100} = 0.1045$

$\overline{q} = 1 - 0.1045 = 0.8955$

$H_0$: $p_1 = p_2$    (claim)
$H_1$: $p_1 \neq p_2$

C. V. $= \pm 1.96$    $\alpha = 0.05$

$z = \dfrac{(0.15 - 0.05) - 0}{\sqrt{(0.1045)(0.8955)(\frac{1}{120} + \frac{1}{100})}} = 2.41$

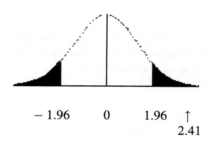

$-1.96$      0      1.96    ↑
                            2.41

Reject the null hypothesis. There is enough evidence to support the claim that the proportion has changed.

For the 95% confidence interval:
$\hat{p}_1 = 0.15$        $\hat{q}_1 = 0.85$
$\hat{p}_2 = 0.05$        $\hat{q}_2 = 0.95$

**15. continued**

$$(0.15 - 0.05) - 1.96\sqrt{\frac{(0.15)(0.85)}{120} + \frac{(0.05)(0.95)}{100}}$$

$$< p_1 - p_2 < (0.15 - 0.05) + 1.96\sqrt{\frac{(0.15)(0.85)}{120} + \frac{(0.05)(0.95)}{100}}$$

$$0.10 - 1.96(0.0392) < p_1 - p_2 <$$

$$0.10 + 1.96(0.0392)$$

$$0.023 < p_1 - p_2 < 0.177$$

## CHAPTER 9 QUIZ

1. False, there are different formulas for independent and dependent samples.
2. False, the samples are independent.
3. True
4. False, they can be right, left, or two tailed.
5. d
6. a
7. c
8. b
9. $\mu_1 = \mu_2$
10. Pooled
11. Normal
12. Negative
13. $\frac{s_1^2}{s_2^2}$

14. $H_0$: $\mu_1 = \mu_2$
$H_1$: $\mu_1 \neq \mu_2$ (claim)
C. V. = $\pm 2.58$    z = $-3.69$
Reject the null hypothesis. There is enough evidence to support the claim that there is a difference in the cholesterol levels of the two groups.
99% Confidence Interval:
$-10.2 < \mu_1 - \mu_2 < -1.8$

15. $H_0$: $\mu_1 \leq \mu_2$
$H_1$: $\mu_1 > \mu_2$ (claim)
C. V. = 1.28       z = 1.60
Reject the null hypothesis. There is enough evidence to support the claim that average rental fees for the eastern apartments is greater than the average rental fees for the western apartments.

16. $H_0$: $\sigma_1^2 = \sigma_2^2$
$H_1$: $\sigma_1^2 \neq \sigma_1^2$ (claim)
F = 1.637        P-value > 0.20 (0.357)

**16. continued**
Do not reject the null hypothesis since P-value > 0.05. There is not enough evidence to support the claim that the variances are different.

17. $H_0$: $\sigma_1^2 = \sigma_2^2$
$H_1$: $\sigma_1^2 \neq \sigma_2^2$ (claim)
C. V. = 1.90       F = 1.296
Do not reject the null hypothesis. There is not enough evidence to support the claim that the variances are different.

18. $H_0$: $\sigma_1 = \sigma_2$ (claim)
$H_1$ $\sigma_1 \neq \sigma_2$
C. V. = 3.53       F = 1.13
Do not reject the null hypothesis. There is not enough evidence to reject the claim that the standard deviations of the number of hours of television viewing are the same.

19. $H_0$: $\sigma_1^2 = \sigma_2^2$
$H_1$ $\sigma_1^2 \neq \sigma_2^2$ (claim)
C. V. = 3.01       F = 1.94
Do not reject the null hypothesis. There is not enough evidence to support the claim that the variances are different.

20. $H_0$: $\sigma_1^2 \leq \sigma_2^2$
$H_1$ $\sigma_1^2 > \sigma_2^2$ (claim)
C. V. = 5.05       F = 1.08
Do not reject the null hypothesis. There is not enough evidence to support the claim that the variance of the number of murders committed on the East Coast is greater than the variance of the number of murders committed on the West Coast. One factor that could influence the results is the populations of the cities that were selected.

21. $H_0$: $\sigma_1 = \sigma_2$
$H_1$ $\sigma_1 \neq \sigma_2$ (claim)
C. V. = 2.46       F = 1.65
Do not reject the null hypothesis. There is not enough evidence to support the claim that the standard deviations are different.

22. $H_0$: $\sigma_1^2 = \sigma_2^2$
$H_1$ $\sigma_1^2 \neq \sigma_2^2$
C. V. = 5.05       F = 1.23
Do not reject. The variances are equal.

$H_0$: $\mu_1 = \mu_2$
$H_1$: $\mu_1 \neq \mu_2$ (claim)

22. continued
C. V. $= \pm 2.779$     $t = 10.922$
Reject the null hypothesis. There is enough evidence to support the claim that the average prices are different.

99% Confidence Interval:
$0.298 < \mu_1 - \mu_2 < 0.502$

23. $H_0$: $\sigma_1^2 = \sigma_2^2$
$H_1$ $\sigma_1^2 \neq \sigma_2^2$
C. V. $= 9.6$     $F = 5.71$
Do not reject. The variances are equal.

$H_0$: $\mu_1 \geq \mu_2$
$H_1$: $\mu_1 < \mu_2$ (claim)
C. V. $= -1.860$     $t = -4.05$
Reject the null hypothesis. There is enough evidence to support the claim that accidents have increased.

24. $H_0$: $\sigma_1^2 = \sigma_2^2$
$H_1$ $\sigma_1^2 \neq \sigma_2^2$
C. V. $= 4.02$     $F = 6.155$
Reject. The variances are unequal.

$H_0$: $\mu_1 = \mu_2$
$H_1$: $\mu_1 \neq \mu_2$ (claim)
C. V. $= \pm 2.718$     $t = 9.807$
Reject the null hypothesis. There is enough evidence to support the claim that the salaries are different.

98% Confidence Interval:
$\$6653 < \mu_1 - \mu_2 < \$11,757$

25. $H_0$: $\sigma_1^2 = \sigma_2^2$
$H_1$ $\sigma_1^2 \neq \sigma_2^2$
$F = 23.08$     P-value $< 0.05$
Reject. The variances are unequal.

$H_0$: $\mu_1 \leq \mu_2$
$H_1$: $\mu_1 > \mu_2$ (claim)
$t = 0.874$   $0.10 <$ P-value $< 0.25$ (0.198)
Do not reject the null hypothesis since P-value $> 0.05$. There is not enough evidence to support the claim that incomes of city residents is greater than incomes of rural residents.

26. $H_0$: $\mu_1 \geq \mu_2$
$H_1$: $\mu_1 < \mu_2$ (claim)
$\overline{D} = -6.5$     $s_D = 4.93$
C. V. $= -2.821$     $t = -4.172$

26. continued
Reject the null hypothesis. There is enough evidence to support the claim that the sessions improved math skills.

27. $H_0$: $\mu_1 \geq \mu_2$
$H_1$: $\mu_1 < \mu_2$ (claim)
$\overline{D} = -0.8$     $s_D = 1.48$
C. V. $= -1.833$     $t = -1.714$
Do not reject the null hypothesis. There is not enough evidence to support the claim that egg production increased.

28. $H_0$: $p_1 = p_2$
$H_1$: $p_1 \neq p_2$ (claim)
C. V. $= \pm 1.65$   $z = -0.69$
Do not reject the null hypothesis. There is not enough evidence to support the claim that the proportions are different.

90% Confidence Interval:
$-0.105 < p_1 - p_2 < 0.045$

29. $H_0$: $p_1 = p_2$ (claim)
$H_1$: $p_1 \neq p_2$
C. V. $= \pm 1.96$   $z = 0.544$
Do not reject the null hypothesis. There is not enough evidence to support the claim that the proportions have changed.

95% Confidence Interval:
$-0.026 < p_1 - p_2 < 0.0460$

Yes, the confidence interval contains 0; hence, the null hypothesis is not rejected.

# Chapter 10 - Correlation and Regression

Note: Graphs are not to scale and are intended to convey a general idea.

Answers may vary due to rounding, TI-83's, or computer programs.

EXERCISE SET 10-2

**1.**
Two variables are related when there exists a discernible pattern between them.

**3.**
$r$, $\rho$ (rho)

**5.**
A positive relationship means that as x increases, y also increases.
A negative relationship means that as x increases, y decreases.

**7.**
Answers will vary.

**9.**
Pearson's Product Moment Correlation Coefficient.

**11.**
There are many other possibilities, such as chance, relationship to a third variable, etc.

**13.**

**Age vs. Exercise**

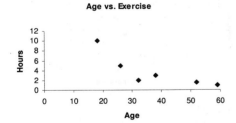

$\sum x = 225$
$\sum y = 22.5$
$\sum x^2 = 9653$
$\sum y^2 = 141.25$
$\sum xy = 625$
$n = 6$
$r = \dfrac{n(\sum xy)-(\sum x)(\sum y)}{\sqrt{[n(\sum x^2)-(\sum x)^2]\,[n(\sum y^2)-(\sum y)^2]}}$

$r = \dfrac{6(625)-(225)(22.5)}{\sqrt{[6(9653)-(225)^2]\,[6(141.25)-(22.5)^2]}}$

$r = -0.832$

**13. continued**
$H_0$: $\rho = 0$
$H_1$: $\rho \neq 0$
C. V. $= \pm 0.811$    d. f. $= 4$
Decision: Reject. There is a significant linear relationship between a person's age and the number of hours a person exercises.

**15.**

**Years vs. Contributions**

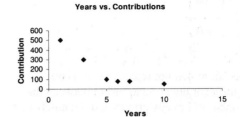

$\sum x = 32$
$\sum y = 1105$
$\sum x^2 = 220$
$\sum y^2 = 364,525$
$\sum xy = 3405$
$n = 6$
$r = \dfrac{n(\sum xy)-(\sum x)(\sum y)}{\sqrt{[n(\sum x^2)-(\sum x)^2]\,[n(\sum y^2)-(\sum y)^2]}}$

$r = \dfrac{6(3405)-(32)(1105)}{\sqrt{[6(220)-(32)^2][6(364525)-(1105)^2]}}$

$r = -0.883$

$H_0$: $\rho = 0$
$H_1$: $\rho \neq 0$
C. V. $= \pm 0.811$    d. f. $= 4$
Decision: Reject. There is a significant linear relationship between the number of years a person has been out of school and his or her contribution.

**17.**

**Larceny vs. Vandalism**

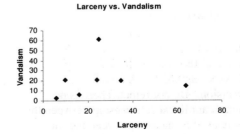

$\sum x = 180$
$\sum y = 147$
$\sum x^2 = 6914$

17. continued
$\sum y^2 = 5273$
$\sum xy = 4013$
n = 7
$$r = \frac{n(\sum xy)-(\sum x)(\sum y)}{\sqrt{[n(\sum x^2)-(\sum x)^2][n(\sum y^2)-(\sum y)^2]}}$$

$$r = \frac{7(4013)-(180)(147)}{\sqrt{[7(6914)-(180)^2][7(5273)-(147)^2]}}$$

$r = 0.104$

$H_0$: $\rho = 0$
$H_1$: $\rho \neq 0$
C. V. = $\pm 0.754$    d. f. = 5
Decision: Do not reject. There is no significant linear relationship between the number of larceny crimes and the number of vandalism crimes committed on college campuses in southwestern Pennsylvania.

19.

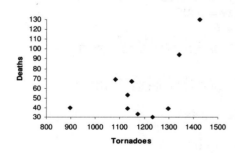

$\sum x = 11,863$
$\sum y = 594$
$\sum x^2 = 14,269,779$
$\sum y^2 = 44,426$
$\sum xy = 729,721$
n = 10
$$r = \frac{10(729,721)-(11,863)(594)}{\sqrt{[10(14,269,779-(11,863)^2][10(44,426)-(594)^2]}}$$

$r = 0.580$

$H_0$: $\rho = 0$
$H_1$: $\rho \neq 0$
C. V. = $\pm 0.632$    d. f. = 8
Decision: Do not reject. There is no significant linear relationship between the number of tornadoes per year and the number of deaths per year from these tornadoes.

21.

$\sum x = 1862$
$\sum y = 3222$
$\sum x^2 = 1,026,026$
$\sum y^2 = 3,009,596$
$\sum xy = 1,754,975$
n = 6
$$r = \frac{n(\sum xy)-(\sum x)(\sum y)}{\sqrt{[n(\sum x^2)-(\sum x)^2][n(\sum y^2)-(\sum y)^2]}}$$

$$r = \frac{6(1,754,975)-(1862)(3222)}{\sqrt{[6(1,026,026)-1862^2][6(3,009,596)-3222^2]}}$$

$r = 0.997$

$H_0$: $\rho = 0$
$H_1$: $\rho \neq 0$
C. V. = $\pm 0.811$    d. f. = 4
Decision: Reject. There is a significant linear relationship between the under 5 age group and the 65 and over age group.

23.

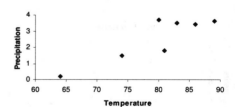

$\sum x = 557$
$\sum y = 17.7$
$\sum x^2 = 44,739$
$\sum y^2 = 55.99$
$\sum xy = 1468.9$
n = 7
$$r = \frac{n(\sum xy)-(\sum x)(\sum y)}{\sqrt{[n(\sum x^2)-(\sum x)^2][n(\sum y^2)-(\sum y)^2]}}$$

$$r = \frac{7(1468.9)-(557)(17.7)}{\sqrt{[7(44,739)-557^2][7(55.99)-17.7^2]}}$$

$r = 0.883$

23. continued
$H_0$: $\rho = 0$
$H_1$: $\rho \neq 0$
C. V. = $\pm 0.754$     d. f. = 5
Decision: Reject. There is a significant linear relationship between the average daily temperature and the average monthly precipitation.

25.

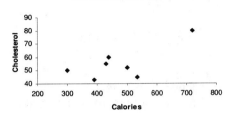

Calories vs. Cholesterol

$\sum x = 3315$
$\sum y = 385$
$\sum x^2 = 1{,}675{,}225$
$\sum y^2 = 22{,}103$
$\sum xy = 189{,}495$
n = 7
$r = \dfrac{n(\sum xy)-(\sum x)(\sum y)}{\sqrt{[n(\sum x^2)-(\sum x)^2]\,[n(\sum y^2)-(\sum y)^2]}}$

$r = \dfrac{7(189{,}495)-(3315)(385)}{\sqrt{[7(1{,}675{,}225)-(3315)^2][7(22{,}103)-(385)^2]}}$

$r = 0.725$

$H_0$: $\rho = 0$
$H_1$: $\rho \neq 0$
C. V. = $\pm 0.754$     d. f. = 5
Decision: Do not reject. There is a no significant linear relationship between the number of calories and the cholesterol content of fast-food chicken sandwiches.

27.

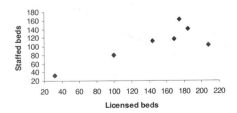

Licensed Beds vs. Staffed Beds

$\sum x = 1013$
$\sum y = 748$
$\sum x^2 = 168{,}435$

27. continued
$\sum y^2 = 90{,}626$
$\sum xy = 120{,}953$
n = 7
$r = \dfrac{7(120{,}953)-(1013)(748)}{\sqrt{[7(168{,}435)-(1013)^2]\,[7(90{,}626)-(748)^2]}}$

$r = 0.831$

$H_0$: $\rho = 0$
$H_1$: $\rho \neq 0$
C. V. = $\pm 0.754$     d. f. = 5
Decision: Reject. There is a significant linear relationship between the number of licensed beds in a hospital and the number of staffed beds.

29.
$r = \dfrac{n(\sum xy)-(\sum x)(\sum y)}{\sqrt{[n(\sum x^2)-(\sum x)^2]\,[n(\sum y^2)-(\sum y)^2]}}$

$r = \dfrac{5(125)-(15)(35)}{\sqrt{[5(55)-(15)^2][5(285)-(35)^2]}} = 1$

$r = \dfrac{5(125)-(35)(15)}{\sqrt{[5(285)-(35)^2][5(55)-(15)^2]}} = 1$

The value of $r$ does not change when the values for x and y are interchanged.

EXERCISE 10-3

1.
Draw the scatter plot and test the significance of the correlation coefficient.

3.
$y' = a + bx$

5.
It is the line that is drawn through the points on the scatter plot such that the sum of the squares of the vertical distances each point is from the line is at a minimum.

7.
When $r$ is positive, $b$ will be positive. When $r$ is negative, $b$ will be negative.

9.
The closer $r$ is to $+1$ or $-1$, the more accurate the predicted value will be.

11.
When $r$ is not significant, the mean of the $y$ values should be used to predict $y$.

**13.**

$$a = \frac{(\sum y)(\sum x^2) - (\sum x)(\sum xy)}{n(\sum x^2) - (\sum x)^2}$$

$$a = \frac{(22.5)(9653) - (225)(625)}{6(9653) - (225)^2} = 10.499$$

$$b = \frac{n(\sum xy) - (\sum x)(\sum y)}{n(\sum x^2) - (\sum x)^2}$$

$$b = \frac{6(625) - (225)(22.5)}{6(9653) - (225)^2} = -0.18$$

$y' = a + bx$
$y' = 10.499 - 0.18x$
$y' = 10.499 - 0.18(35) = 4.199$ hours or
4.2 hours

**15.**

$$a = \frac{(\sum y)(\sum x^2) - (\sum x)(\sum xy)}{n(\sum x^2) - (\sum x)^2}$$

$$a = \frac{(1105)(220) - (32)(3405)}{6(220) - (32)^2}$$

$$a = \frac{243100 - 108960}{1320 - 1024} = \frac{134140}{296} = 453.176$$

$$b = \frac{n(\sum xy) - (\sum x)(\sum y)}{n(\sum x^2) - (\sum x)^2}$$

$$b = \frac{6(3405) - (32)(1105)}{6(220) - (32)^2} = \frac{20430 - 35360}{296}$$

$$b = \frac{-14930}{296} = -50.439$$

$y' = a + bx$
$y' = 453.176 - 50.439x$
$y' = 453.176 - 50.439(4) = \$251.42$

**17.**
Since $r$ is not significant, no regression should be done.

**19.**
Since r is not significant, no regression should be done.

**21.**

$$a = \frac{(\sum y)(\sum x^2) - (\sum x)(\sum xy)}{n(\sum x^2) - (\sum x)^2}$$

$$a = \frac{(3222)(1026026) - (1862)(1754975)}{6(1026026) - (1862)^2}$$

$$a = 14.165$$

$$b = \frac{n(\sum xy) - (\sum x)(\sum y)}{n(\sum x^2) - (\sum x)^2}$$

$$b = \frac{6(1754975) - (1862)(3222)}{6(1026026) - (1862)^2} = 1.685$$

**21. continued**
$y' = a + bx$
$y' = 14.165 + 1.685x$
$y' = 14.165 + 1.685(200) = 351$ under 5.

**23.**

$$a = \frac{(\sum y)(\sum x^2) - (\sum x)(\sum xy)}{n(\sum x^2) - (\sum x)^2}$$

$$a = \frac{(17.7)(44739) - (557)(1468.9)}{7(44739) - (557)^2} = -8.994$$

$$b = \frac{n(\sum xy) - (\sum x)(\sum y)}{n(\sum x^2) - (\sum x)^2}$$

$$b = \frac{7(1468.9) - (557)(17.7)}{7(44739) - (557)^2} = 0.1448$$

$y' = a + bx$
$y' = -8.994 + 0.1448x$
$y' = -8.994 + 0.1448(70) = 1.1$ inches

**25.**
Since $r$ is not significant, no regression should be done.

**27.**

$$a = \frac{(\sum y)(\sum x^2) - (\sum x)(\sum xy)}{n(\sum x^2) - (\sum x)^2}$$

$$a = \frac{(748)(168,435) - (1013)(120,953)}{7(168,435) - (1013)^2}$$
$$a = 22.659$$

$$b = \frac{n(\sum xy) - (\sum x)(\sum y)}{n(\sum x^2) - (\sum x)^2}$$

$$b = \frac{7(120,953) - (1013)(748)}{7(168,435) - (1013)^2} = 0.582$$

$y' = a + bx$
$y' = 22.659 + 0.582x$
$y' = 22.659 + 0.582(44) = 48.267$ staffed beds

**29.**

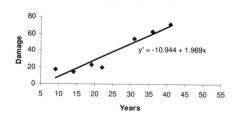

$\sum x = 172$
$\sum y = 262$
$\sum x^2 = 5060$
$\sum y^2 = 13340$

29. continued

$\sum xy = 8079$

$n = 7$

$r = \dfrac{n(\sum xy)-(\sum x)(\sum y)}{\sqrt{[n(\sum x^2)-(\sum x)^2]\,[n(\sum y^2)-(\sum y)^2]}}$

$r = \dfrac{7(8079)-(172)(262)}{\sqrt{[7(5060)-(172)^2][7(13340)-(262)^2]}} = 0.956$

$H_0$: $\rho = 0$

$H_1$: $\rho \neq 0$

C. V. $= \pm 0.754$     d. f. $= 5$

Decision:  Reject

There is a significant relationship between the number of years a person smokes and the amount of lung damage.

$a = \dfrac{(\sum y)(\sum x^2)-(\sum x)(\sum xy)}{n(\sum x^2)-(\sum x)^2}$

$a = \dfrac{(262)(5060)-(172)(8079)}{7(5060)-(172)^2} = -10.944$

$b = \dfrac{n(\sum xy)-(\sum x)(\sum y)}{n(\sum x^2)-(\sum x)^2}$

$b = \dfrac{7(8079)-(172)(262)}{7(5060)-(172)^2} = 1.969$

$y' = a + bx$

$y' = -10.944 + 1.969x$

$y' = -10.944 + 1.969(30) = 48.126\%$

31.

Tons of Coal vs. Number of Employees

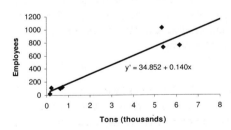

$y' = 34.852 + 0.140x$

$\sum x = 26,728$

$\sum y = 4027$

$\sum x^2 = 162,101,162$

$\sum y^2 = 3,550,103$

$\sum xy = 23,663,669$

$n = 8$

$r = \dfrac{n(\sum xy)-(\sum x)(\sum y)}{\sqrt{[n(\sum x^2)-(\sum x)^2]\,[n(\sum y^2)-(\sum y)^2]}}$

$r = \dfrac{8(23662669)-(26728)(4027)}{\sqrt{[8(162101162)-26728^2][8(3550103)-(4027)^2]}}$

$r = 0.970$

31. continued

$H_0$: $\rho = 0$

$H_1$: $\rho \neq 0$

C. V. $= \pm 0.707$     d. f. $= 6$

Decision:  Reject. There is a significant relationship between the number of tons of coal produced and the number of employees.

$a = \dfrac{(\sum y)(\sum x^2)-(\sum x)(\sum xy)}{n(\sum x^2)-(\sum x)^2}$

$a = \dfrac{(4027)(162101162)-(26728)(23663669)}{8(162101162)-(26728)^2}$

$a = 34.852$

$b = \dfrac{n(\sum xy)-(\sum x)(\sum y)}{n(\sum x^2)-(\sum x)^2}$

$b = \dfrac{8(23663669)-(26728)(4027)}{8(162101162)-(26728)^2} = 0.140$

$y' = a + bx$

$y' = 34.852 + 0.140x$

$y' = 34.852 + 0.140(500) = 104.9$

33.

Absences vs. Final Grades

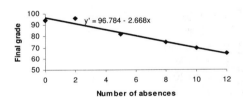

$y' = 96.784 - 2.668x$

$\sum x = 37$

$\sum y = 482$

$\sum x^2 = 337$

$\sum y^2 = 39526$

$\sum xy = 2682$

$n = 6$

$r = \dfrac{n(\sum xy)-(\sum x)(\sum y)}{\sqrt{[n(\sum x^2)-(\sum x)^2]\,[n(\sum y^2)-(\sum y)^2]}}$

$r = \dfrac{6(2682)-(37)(482)}{\sqrt{[6(337)-(37)^2][6(39526)-(482)^2]}}$

$r = -0.981$

$H_0$: $\rho = 0$

$H_1$: $\rho \neq 0$

C. V. $= \pm 0.811$     d. f. $= 4$

Decision:  Reject. There is a significant relationship between the number of absences and the final grade.

**33. continued**

$$a = \frac{(\sum y)(\sum x^2) - (\sum x)(\sum xy)}{n(\sum x^2) - (\sum x)^2}$$

$$a = \frac{(482)(337) - (37)(2682)}{6(337) - (37)^2} = 96.784$$

$$b = \frac{n(\sum xy) - (\sum x)(\sum y)}{n(\sum x^2) - (\sum x)^2}$$

$$b = \frac{6(2682) - (37)(482)}{6(337) - (37)^2} = -2.668$$

$y' = a + bx$
$y' = 96.784 - 2.668x$

**35.**

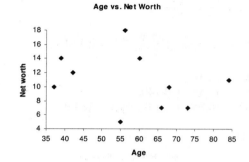

$\sum x = 580$
$\sum y = 108$
$\sum x^2 = 35,780$
$\sum y^2 = 1304$
$\sum xy = 6120$
$n = 10$

$$r = \frac{n(\sum xy) - (\sum x)(\sum y)}{\sqrt{[n(\sum x^2) - (\sum x)^2][n(\sum y^2) - (\sum y)^2]}}$$

$$r = \frac{10(6120) - (580)(108)}{\sqrt{[10(35,780) - 580^2][10(1304) - 108^2]}}$$

$r = -0.265$
$H_0$: $\rho = 0$
$H_1$: $\rho \neq 0$
P-value > 0.05 (0.459)
Decision: Do not reject since P-value > 0.05. There is no significant linear relationship between the ages of billionaires and their net worth. Since $r$ is not significant, no regression should be done.

**37.**
For Exercise 15:
$\bar{x} = 5.3333$
$\bar{y} = 184.1667$
$b = -50.439$
$a = \bar{y} - b\bar{x}$
$a = 184.1667 - (-50.439)(5.3333)$

**37. continued**
$a = 184.1667 + 269.0063$
$a = 453.173$ (differs due to rounding)

For Exercise 16:
$\bar{x} = 40.33$
$\bar{y} = 8.33$
$b = -0.317$
$a = \bar{y} - b\bar{x}$
$a = 8.33 - (-0.317)(40.33)$
$a = 8.33 + 12.78$
$a = 21.11$ or 21.1

**EXERCISE SET 10-4**

**1.**
Explained variation is the variation due to the relationship and is computed by $\sum(y' - \bar{y})^2$.

**3.**
Total variation is the sum of the squares of the vertical distances of the points from the mean. It is computed by $\sum(y - \bar{y})^2$.

**5.**
It is found by squaring $r$.

**7.**
The coefficient of non-determination is $1 - r^2$.

**9.**
For $r = 0.70$, $r^2 = 0.49$ and $1 - r^2 = 0.51$. Thus 49% of the variation of y is due to the variation of x, and 51% of the variation of y is due to chance.

**11.**
For $r = 0.37$, $r^2 = 0.1369$ and $1 - r^2 = 0.8631$. Thus 13.69% of the variation of y is due to the variation of x, and 86.31% of the variation of y is due to chance.

**13.**
For $r = 0.05$, $r^2 = 0.0025$ and $1 - r^2 = 0.9975$. Thus 0.25% of the variation of y is due to the variation of x, and 99.75% of the variation of y is due to chance.

Note: For Exercises 15 − 17, values for $a$ and $b$ are rounded to 3 decimal places according to the textbook's rounding rule for intercept and slope of the regression equation. Where these answers differ from the text, additional decimal places are included to show consistency with text answers.

**15.**

$$S_{est} = \sqrt{\frac{\sum y^2 - a\sum y - b\sum xy}{n-2}}$$

$$S_{est} = \sqrt{\frac{141.25 - 10.499(22.5) - (-0.180)(625)}{6-2}}$$

$$S_{est} = \sqrt{4.38065} = 2.093$$

Using $a = 10.4988$ and $b = -0.17997$,
$S_{est} = 2.09214304$ or $2.092$

**17.**

$$S_{est} = \sqrt{\frac{\sum y^2 - a\sum y - b\sum xy}{n-2}} =$$

$$S_{est} = \sqrt{\frac{364525 - (453.176)(1105) - (-50.439)(3405)}{6-2}}$$

$$S_{est} = 94.22$$

**19.**
$y' = 10.499 - 0.18x$
$y' = 10.499 - 0.18(20)$
$y' = 6.899$

$$y' - t_{\frac{\alpha}{2}} \cdot s_{est}\sqrt{1 + \frac{1}{n} + \frac{n(x-\overline{X})}{n\sum x^2 - (\sum x)^2}} < y <$$

$$y' + t_{\frac{\alpha}{2}} \cdot s_{est}\sqrt{1 + \frac{1}{n} + \frac{n(x-\overline{X})^2}{n\sum x^2 - (\sum x)^2}}$$

$$6.899 - (2.132)(2.09)\sqrt{1 + \frac{1}{6} + \frac{6(20-37.5)^2}{6(9653) - 225^2}} < y <$$

$$< y < 6.899 + (2.132)(2.09)\sqrt{1 + \frac{1}{6} + \frac{6(20-37.5)^2}{6(9653) - 225^2}}$$

$6.899 - (2.132)(2.09)(1.191) < y <$

$6.899 + (2.132)(2.09)(1.91)$

$1.59 < y < 12.21$

**21.**
$y' = 453.176 - 50.439x$
$y' = 453.176 - 50.439(4)$
$y' = 251.42$

**21. continued**

$$y' - t_{\frac{\alpha}{2}} \cdot s_{est}\sqrt{1 + \frac{1}{n} + \frac{n(x-\overline{X})^2}{n\sum x^2 - (\sum x)^2}} < y <$$

$$y' + t_{\frac{\alpha}{2}} \cdot s_{est}\sqrt{1 + \frac{1}{n} + \frac{n(x-\overline{X})^2}{n\sum x^2 - (\sum x)^2}}$$

$$251.42 - 2.132(94.22)\sqrt{1 + \frac{1}{6} + \frac{6(4-5.33)^2}{6(220) - 32^2}}$$

$$< y < 251.42 + 2.132(94.22)\sqrt{1 + \frac{1}{6} + \frac{6(4-5.33)^2}{6(220) - 32^2}}$$

$251.42 - (2.132)(94.22)(1.1) < y <$
$\qquad 251.42 + (2.132)(94.22)(1.1)$
$\$30.46 < y < \$472.38$

**REVIEW EXERCISES - CHAPTER 10**

**1.**

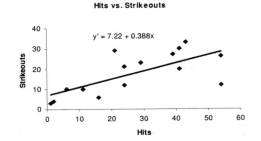

Hits vs. Strikeouts

$y' = 7.22 + 0.388x$

$\sum x = 406$
$\sum y = 266$
$\sum x^2 = 15,416$
$\sum y^2 = 6154$
$\sum xy = 8919$
$n = 15$

$$r = \frac{n(\sum xy) - (\sum x)(\sum y)}{\sqrt{[n(\sum x^2) - (\sum x)^2][n(\sum y^2) - (\sum y)^2]}}$$

$$r = \frac{15(8919) - (406)(266)}{\sqrt{[15(15416) - (406)^2][15(6154) - (266)^2]}}$$

$r = 0.682$

$H_0: \rho = 0$
$H_1: \rho \neq 0$
C. V. $= \pm 0.641$      d. f. $= 13$

Decision: Reject. There is a significant linear relationship between the number of hits and the number of strikeouts.

$$a = \frac{(\sum y)(\sum x^2) - (\sum x)(\sum xy)}{n(\sum x^2) - (\sum x)^2}$$

$$a = \frac{(266)(15416) - (406)(8919)}{15(15416) - (406)^2} = 7.222$$

1. continued

$$b = \frac{n(\sum xy) - (\sum x)(\sum y)}{n(\sum x^2) - (\sum x)^2}$$

$$b = \frac{15(8919) - (406)(266)}{15(15416) - (406)^2} = 0.388$$

$y' = a + bx$
$y' = 7.222 + 0.388x$
$y' = 7.222 + 0.388(30) = 18.86$ or 18.9
strikeouts

3.

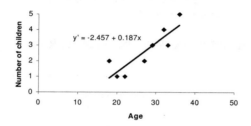

Mother's Age vs. Number of Children

$y' = -2.457 + 0.187x$

$\sum x = 217$
$\sum y = 21$
$\sum x^2 = 6187$
$\sum y^2 = 69$
$\sum xy = 626$
$n = 8$

$$r = \frac{n(\sum xy) - (\sum x)(\sum y)}{\sqrt{[n(\sum x^2) - (\sum x)^2][n(\sum y^2) - (\sum y)^2]}}$$

$$r = \frac{8(626) - (217)(21)}{\sqrt{[8(6187) - (217)^2][8(69) - (21)^2]}}$$

$r = 0.873$

$H_0:\ \rho = 0$
$H_1:\ \rho \neq 0$
C. V. $= \pm 0.834$    d. f. $= 6$

Decision: Reject. There is a significant relationship between the mother's age and the number of children she has.

$$a = \frac{(\sum y)(\sum x^2) - (\sum x)(\sum xy)}{n(\sum x^2) - (\sum x)^2}$$

$$a = \frac{(21)(6187) - (217)(626)}{8(6187) - (217)^2} = -2.457$$

$$b = \frac{n(\sum xy) - (\sum x)(\sum y)}{n(\sum x^2) - (\sum x)^2}$$

$$b = \frac{8(626) - (217)(21)}{8(6187) - (217)^2} = 0.187$$

3. continued

$y' = a + bx$
$y' = -2.457 + 0.187x$
$y' = -2.457 + 0.187(34) = 3.9$

5.

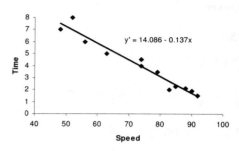

Typing Speeds vs. Learning Times

$y' = 14.086 - 0.137x$

$\sum x = 884$
$\sum y = 47.8$
$\sum x^2 = 67,728$
$\sum y^2 = 242.06$
$\sum xy = 3163.8$
$n = 12$

$$r = \frac{n(\sum xy) - (\sum x)(\sum y)}{\sqrt{[n(\sum x^2) - (\sum x)^2][n(\sum y^2) - (\sum y)^2]}}$$

$$r = \frac{12(3163.8) - (884)(47.8)}{\sqrt{[12(67728) - (884)^2][12(242.06) - (47.8)^2]}}$$

$r = -0.974$

$H_0:\ \rho = 0$
$H_1:\ \rho \neq 0$
C. V. $= \pm 0.708$    d. f. $= 10$

Decision: Reject. There is a significant relationship between speed and time.

$$a = \frac{(\sum y)(\sum x^2) - (\sum x)(\sum xy)}{n(\sum x^2) - (\sum x)^2}$$

$$a = \frac{(47.8)(67728) - (884)(3163.8)}{12(67728) - (884)^2}$$

$a = 14.086$

$$b = \frac{n(\sum xy) - (\sum x)(\sum y)}{n(\sum x^2) - (\sum x)^2}$$

$$b = \frac{12(3163.8) - (884)(47.8)}{12(67728) - (884)^2}$$

$b = -0.137$

$y' = a + bx$
$y' = 14.086 - 0.137x$
$y' = 14.086 - 0.137(72) = 4.222$

7.

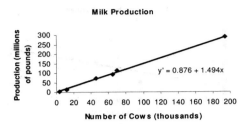

$\sum x = 390$
$\sum y = 588$
$\sum x^2 = 49{,}030$
$\sum y^2 = 110{,}644$
$\sum xy = 73{,}603$
$n = 6$

$$r = \frac{n(\sum xy)-(\sum x)(\sum y)}{\sqrt{[n(\sum x^2)-(\sum x)^2]\,[n(\sum y^2)-(\sum y)^2]}}$$

$$r = \frac{6(73{,}603)-(390)(588)}{\sqrt{[6(49{,}030)-(390)^2][6(110{,}644)-(588)^2]}}$$

$r = 0.999$

$H_0:\ \rho = 0$
$H_1:\ \rho \neq 0$
C. V. $\pm 0.917$     d. f. $= 4$

Decision: Reject. There is a significant relationship between the number of cows and the number of pounds of milk produced in the counties located in southwestern Pennsylvania.

$$a = \frac{(\sum y)(\sum x^2)-(\sum x)(\sum xy)}{n(\sum x^2)-(\sum x)^2}$$

$$a = \frac{(588)(49{,}030)-(390)(73{,}603)}{6(49{,}030)-(390)^2}$$

$a = 0.876$

$$b = \frac{n(\sum xy)-(\sum x)(\sum y)}{n(\sum x^2)-(\sum x)^2}$$

$$b = \frac{6(73{,}603)-(390)(588)}{6(49030)-(390)^2}$$

$b = 1.494$

$y' = a + bx$
$y' = 1.494 + 0.876x$

9.

$$S_{est} = \sqrt{\frac{\sum y^2 - a\sum y - b\sum xy}{n-2}}$$

$$S_{est} = \sqrt{\frac{242.06 - 14.086(47.8) + 0.137(3163.8)}{12-2}}$$

9. continued
$$S_{est} = \sqrt{\frac{2.1898}{10}} = \sqrt{0.21898} = 0.468$$

(Note:  TI-83 calculator answer is 0.513)

11.
(For calculation purposes only, since no regression should be done.)

$y' = 14.086 - 0.137x$
$y' = 14.086 - 0.137(72) = 4.222$

$$y' - t_{\frac{\alpha}{2}} \cdot S_{est}\sqrt{1 + \tfrac{1}{n} + \frac{n(x-\overline{X})^2}{n\Sigma x^2-(\Sigma x)^2}} < y <$$

$$y' + t_{\frac{\alpha}{2}} \cdot S_{est}\sqrt{1 + \tfrac{1}{n} + \frac{n(x-\overline{X})^2}{n\Sigma x^2-(\Sigma x)^2}}$$

$$4.222 - 1.812(0.468)\sqrt{1 + \tfrac{1}{12} + \frac{12(72-73.667)^2}{12(67{,}728)-884^2}}$$
$$< y < 4.222 + 1.812(0.468)\sqrt{1 + \tfrac{1}{12} + \frac{12(72-73.667)^2}{12(67{,}728)-884^2}}$$

$$4.222 - 1.812(0.468)(1.041) < y <$$
$$4.222 + 1.812(0.468)(1.041)$$
$3.34 < y < 5.10$

## CHAPTER 10 QUIZ

1. False, the y variable would decrease.
2. True
3. True
4. False, the relationship may be affected by another variable, or by chance.
5. False, a relationship may be caused by chance.
6. False, there are several independent variables and one dependent variable.
7. a
8. a
9. d
10. c
11. b
12. Scatter plot
13. Independent
14. $-1, +1$
15. b
16. Line of best fit
17. $+1, -1$

18.

Price Comparison of Drugs

$\sum x = 18.61$
$\sum x^2 = 51.1919$
$\sum y = 7.67$
$\sum y^2 = 9.2083$
$\sum xy = 21.0956$
n = 7
r = 0.600
$H_0$: $\rho = 0$
$H_1$: $\rho \neq 0$
C.V. = $\pm 0.754$    d. f. = 5
Do not reject. There is no significant linear relationship between the price of the same drugs in the United States and in Australia. No regression should be done.

19.

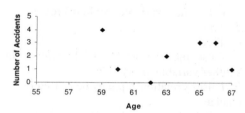

Age vs. Number of Accidents

$\sum x = 442$
$\sum x^2 = 27,964$
$\sum y = 14$
$\sum y^2 = 40$
$\sum xy = 882$
n = 7
r = $-0.078$
$H_0$: $\rho = 0$
$H_1$: $\rho \neq 0$
C. V. = $\pm 0.754$    d. f. = 5
Decision: Do not reject. There is not a significant relationship between age and number of accidents. No regression should be done.

20.

Age vs. Number of Cavities

$\sum x = 59$
$\sum x^2 = 621$
$\sum y = 21$
$\sum y^2 = 91$
$\sum xy = 229$
n = 6
r = 0.842
$H_0$: $\rho = 0$
$H_1$: $\rho \neq 0$
C. V. = $\pm 0.811$    d. f. = 4
Decision: Reject. There is a significant linear relationship between age and number of cavities.
a = $-1.918$        b = 0.551
$y' = -1.918 + 0.551x$
When x = 11:  $y' = -1.918 + 0.551(11)$
$y' = 4.14$ or 4 cavities

21.

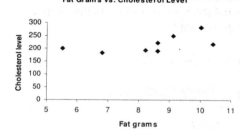

Fat Grams vs. Cholesterol Level

$\sum x = 67.2$
$\sum x^2 = 582.62$
$\sum y = 1740$
$\sum y^2 = 386,636$
$\sum xy = 14847.9$
n = 8
r = 0.602
$H_0$: $\rho = 0$
$H_1$: $\rho \neq 0$
C. V. = $\pm 0.707$    d. f. = 6
Decision: Do not reject. There is no significant linear relationship between fat and cholesterol. No regression should be done.

22.
$$S_{est} = \sqrt{\frac{91-(-1.918)(21)-0.551(229)}{6-2}}$$
$S_{est} = 1.129*$

23.
(For calculation purposes only, since no regression should be done.)

$$S_{est} = \sqrt{\frac{386,636-110.12(1740)-12.784(14,847.9)}{8-2}}$$
$S_{est} = 29.47*$

24.
$y' = -1.918 + 0.551(7) = 1.939$ or 2

$$2 - 2.132(1.129)\sqrt{1+\frac{1}{6}+\frac{6(11-9.833)^2}{6(621)-59^2}} < y$$

$$< 2 + 2.132(1.129)\sqrt{1+\frac{1}{6}+\frac{6(11-9.833)^2}{6(621)-59^2}}$$

$$2 - 2.132(1.129)(1.095) < y < 2 + 2.132(1.129)(1.095)$$

$-0.6 < y < 4.6$ or $0 < y < 5*$

25.
Since no regression should be done, the average of the $y'$ values is used: 217.5

Note: Graphs are not to scale and are intended to convey a general idea.

Answers may vary due to rounding, TI-83's, or computer programs.

EXERCISE SET 11-2

1.
The variance test compares a sample variance to a hypothesized population variance, while the goodness of fit test compares a distribution obtained from a sample with a hypothesized distribution.

3.
The expected values are computed based on what the null hypothesis states about the distribution.

5.
$H_0$: The ages of automobiles are equally distributed over the three categories. (claim)
$H_1$: The ages of automobiles are not equally distributed over the three categories.
C. V. = 5.991    d. f. = 2    $\alpha = 0.05$
$E = \frac{30}{3} = 10$
$\chi^2 = \sum \frac{(O - E)^2}{E} = \frac{(8-10)^2}{10} + \frac{(10-10)^2}{10} +$

$\frac{(12-10)^2}{10} = 0.8$

Alternate Solution:

| O | E | O − E | $(O - E)^2$ | $\frac{(O-E)^2}{E}$ |
|---|---|---|---|---|
| 8 | 10 | -2 | 4 | 0.4 |
| 10 | 10 | 0 | 0 | 0 |
| 12 | 10 | 2 | 4 | 0.4 |
| | | | | 0.8 |

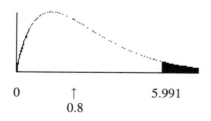

0          ↑          5.991
          0.8

Do not reject the null hypothesis. There is not enough evidence to reject the claim that the average age of automobiles is equally distributed over the three categories. Tire manufacturers need to make enough tires to fit automobiles of all ages.

7.
$H_0$: The proportions are distributed as follows: 28.1% purchased a small car, 47.8% purchased a mid-sized car, 7% purchased a large car, and 17.1% purchased a luxury car.
$H_1$: The distribution is not the same as stated in the null hypothesis. (claim)
C. V. = 7.815    d. f. = 3    $\alpha = 0.05$

$\chi^2 = \sum \frac{(O-E)^2}{E} = \frac{(25-28.1)^2}{28.1} + \frac{(50-47.8)^2}{47.8}$

$+ \frac{(10-7)^2}{7} + \frac{(15-17.1)^2}{17.1} = 1.9869$

Alternate Solution:

| O | E | O − E | $(O - E)^2$ | $\frac{(O-E)^2}{E}$ |
|---|---|---|---|---|
| 25 | 28.1 | -3.1 | 9.61 | 0.3420 |
| 50 | 47.8 | 2.2 | 4.84 | 0.1013 |
| 10 | 7 | 3 | 9 | 1.2857 |
| 15 | 17.1 | -2.1 | 4.41 | 0.2579 |
| | | | | 1.9869 |

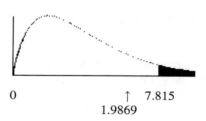

0                    ↑    7.815
                  1.9869

Do not reject the null hypothesis. There is not enough evidence to support the claim that the proportions are different.

9.
$H_0$: The proportions are distributed as follows: safe - 35%, not safe - 52%, no opinion - 13%.
$H_1$: The distribution is not the same as stated in the null hypothesis. (claim)
C. V. = 9.210    d. f. = 2    $\alpha = 0.01$

$\chi^2 = \frac{(40-42)^2}{42} + \frac{(60-62.4)^2}{62.4} + \frac{(20-15.6)^2}{15.6}$

$\chi^2 = 1.4286$

Alternate Solution:

| O | E | O − E | $(O - E)^2$ | $\frac{(O-E)^2}{E}$ |
|---|---|---|---|---|
| 40 | 42 | -2 | 4 | 0.09524 |
| 60 | 62.4 | -2.4 | 5.76 | 0.09231 |
| 20 | 15.6 | 4.4 | 19.36 | 1.24103 |
| | | | | 1.42858 |

9. continued

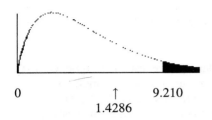

0      ↑         9.210
    1.4286

Do not reject the null hypothesis. There is not enough evidence to support the claim that the proportions are different.

11.
$H_0$: The distribution of loans is as follows: 21% - mortgages, 39% - autos, 20% - credit card, 12% - real estate, and 8% - miscellaneous. (claim)
$H_1$: The distribution is not the same as stated in the null hypothesis.
C. V. = 9.488    d. f. = 4    $\alpha = 0.05$
$\chi^2 = \frac{(25-21)^2}{21} + \frac{(44-39)^2}{39} + \frac{(19-20)^2}{20} +$

$\frac{(8-12)^2}{12} + \frac{(4-8)^2}{8} = 4.7862$

Alternate Solution:

| O | E | O − E | (O − E)² | $\frac{(O-E)^2}{E}$ |
|---|---|---|---|---|
| 25 | 21 | 4 | 16 | 0.7619 |
| 44 | 39 | 5 | 25 | 0.6410 |
| 19 | 20 | -1 | 1 | 0.05 |
| 8 | 12 | -4 | 16 | 1.3333 |
| 4 | 8 | -4 | 16 | 2.0000 |
| | | | | 4.7862 |

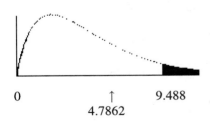

0          ↑         9.488
        4.7862

Do not reject the null hypothesis. There is not enough evidence to reject the claim that the distribution is the same.

13.
$H_0$: The methods of payment for purchases are distributed as follows: 53% use cash, 30% use checks, 16% use credit cards, and 1% have no preference. (claim)

13. continued
$H_1$: The distribution is not the same as stated in the null hypothesis.
C. V. = 11.345    d. f. = 3    $\alpha = 0.01$

$\chi^2 = \frac{(400-424)^2}{424} + \frac{(210-240)^2}{240} + \frac{(170-128)^2}{128}$

$+ \frac{(20-8)^2}{8} = 36.8897$

Alternate Solution:

| O | E | O − E | (O − E)² | $\frac{(O-E)^2}{E}$ |
|---|---|---|---|---|
| 400 | 424 | -24 | 576 | 1.35849 |
| 210 | 240 | -30 | 900 | 3.7500 |
| 170 | 128 | 42 | 1764 | 13.78125 |
| 20 | 8 | 12 | 144 | 18.0000 |
| | | | | 36.88974 |

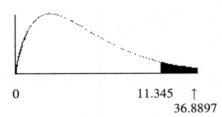

0                11.345    ↑
                        36.8897

Reject the null hypothesis. There is enough evidence to reject the claim that the distribution is the same as reported in the survey.

15.
$H_0$: The distribution is as follows: violent offenses - 29.5%, property offenses - 29%, drug offenses - 30.2%, weapons offenses - 10.6%, other offenses - 0.7%. (claim)
$H_1$: The distribution is not the same as stated in the null hypothesis.
C. V. = 9.488    d. f. = 4    $\alpha = 0.05$

$\chi^2 = \sum \frac{(O-E)^2}{E} = \frac{(298-295)^2}{295} + \frac{(275-290)^2}{290}$

$+ \frac{(344-302)^2}{302} + \frac{(80-106)^2}{106} + \frac{(3-7)^2}{7}$

$\chi^2 = 15.3106$ or $15.31$

Alternate Solution:

15. continued

| O | E | O − E | $(O-E)^2$ | $\frac{(O-E)^2}{E}$ |
|---|---|---|---|---|
| 298 | 295 | 3 | 9 | 0.0305 |
| 275 | 290 | -15 | 225 | 0.7759 |
| 344 | 302 | 42 | 1764 | 5.8411 |
| 80 | 106 | -26 | 676 | 6.3774 |
| 3 | 7 | -4 | 16 | 2.2857 |
| | | | | 15.3106 |

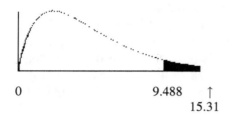

$$0 \qquad\qquad 9.488 \quad \uparrow$$
$$15.31$$

Reject the null hypothesis. There is enough evidence to reject the claim that the proportions are as stated.

17.
$H_0$: The distribution of the ways people pay for their prescriptions is as follows: 60% used personal funds, 25% used insurance, and 15% used Medicare. (claim)
$H_1$: The distribution is not the same as stated in the null hypothesis.
$\alpha = 0.05$    d. f. = 2
P-value > 0.05

$$\chi^2 = \sum \frac{(O-E)^2}{E} = \frac{(32-30)^2}{30} + \frac{(10-12.5)^2}{12.5} +$$

$$\frac{(8-7.5)^2}{7.5} = 0.667$$

Alternate Solution:

| O | E | O − E | $(O-E)^2$ | $\frac{(O-E)^2}{E}$ |
|---|---|---|---|---|
| 32 | 30 | 2 | 4 | 0.133 |
| 10 | 12.5 | -2.5 | 6.25 | 0.5 |
| 8 | 7.5 | 0.5 | 0.25 | 0.033 |
| | | | | 0.666* |

*differs due to rounding

Do not reject the null hypothesis since P-value > 0.05. There is not enough evidence to reject the claim that the distribution is the same as stated in the null hypothesis. An implication of the results is that the majority of people are using their own money to pay for medications. A less expensive medication could help people financially.

19.
Answers will vary.

EXERCISE SET 11-3

1.
The independence test and the goodness of fit test both use the same formula for computing the test-value; however, the independence test uses a contingency table whereas the goodness of fit test does not.

3.
$H_0$: The variables are independent or not related.
$H_1$: The variables are dependent or related.

5.
The expected values are computed as (row total · column total) ÷ grand total.

7.
$H_0$: $p_1 = p_2 = p_3 = \cdots = p_n$
$H_1$: At least one proportion is different from the others.

9.
$H_0$: Type of pet owned is independent of annual household income.
$H_1$: Type of pet owned is dependent on annual household income. (claim)

C. V. = 21.026    d. f. = 12    $\alpha = 0.05$

$$E = \frac{(\text{row sum})(\text{column sum})}{\text{grand total}}$$

$$E_{1,1} = \frac{(534)(1003)}{4004} = 133.7667$$

$$E_{1,2} = \frac{(534)(1000)}{4004} = 133.3666$$

$$E_{1,3} = \frac{(534)(1000)}{4004} = 133.3666$$

$$E_{1,4} = \frac{(534)(1001)}{4004} = 133.5$$

$$E_{2,1} = \frac{(800)(1003)}{4004} = 200.3996$$

$$E_{2,2} = \frac{(800)(1000)}{4004} = 199.8002$$

$$E_{2,3} = \frac{(800)(1000)}{4004} = 199.8002$$

$$E_{2,4} = \frac{(800)(1001)}{4004} = 200.0$$

$$E_{3,1} = \frac{(869)(1003)}{4004} = 208.6661$$

9. continued

$E_{3,2} = \frac{(833)(1000)}{4004} = 208.0420$

$E_{3,3} = \frac{(833)(1000)}{4004} = 208.0420$

$E_{3,4} = \frac{(833)(1001)}{4004} = 208.25$

$E_{4,1} = \frac{(968)(1003)}{4004} = 242.2835$

$E_{4,2} = \frac{(968)(1000)}{4004} = 241.7582$

$E_{4,3} = \frac{(968)(1000)}{4004} = 241.7582$

$E_{4,4} = \frac{(968)(1001)}{4004} = 242.0$

### Type of Pet

| Income | Dog | Cat |
|---|---|---|
| < $12,500 | 127(133.7667) | 139(133.3666) |
| $12,500 - $24,999 | 191(199.8002) | 197(199.8002) |
| $25,000 - $39,999 | 216(217.6841) | 215(217.0330) |
| $40,000 - $59,999 | 215(208.6661) | 212(208.0420) |
| $60,000 & over | 254(242.4835) | 237(241.7582) |

| Income | Bird | Horse |
|---|---|---|
| < $12,500 | 173(133.3666) | 95(133.5) |
| $12,500 - $24,999 | 209(199.8002) | 203(200.0) |
| $25,000 -$39,999 | 220(217.0330) | 218(217.25) |
| $40,000 - $59,999 | 175(208.0420) | 231(208.25) |
| $60,000 & over | 223(241.7582) | 254(242.0) |

$\chi^2 = \sum \frac{(O-E)^2}{E} = \frac{(127-133.7667)^2}{133.7667} + \frac{(139-133.3666)^2}{133.3666}$

$+ \frac{(173-133.3666)^2}{133.3666} + \frac{(95-133.5)^2}{133.5} + \frac{(191-199.8002)^2}{199.8002}$

$+ \frac{(197-199.8002)^2}{199.8002} + \frac{(209-199.8002)^2}{199.8002} + \frac{(203-200.0)^2}{200}$

$+ \frac{(216-217.6841)^2}{217.6841} + \frac{(215-217.0330)^2}{217.0330} + \frac{(220-217.0330)^2}{217.0330}$

$+ \frac{(218-217.25))^2}{217.25} + \frac{(215-208.6661)^2}{208.6661} + \frac{(212-208.0420)^2}{208.0420}$

$+ \frac{(175-208.0420)^2}{208.0420} + \frac{(231-208.25)^2}{208.25} + \frac{(254-242.4835)^2}{242.4835}$

$+ \frac{(237-241.7582)^2}{241.7582} + \frac{(223-241.7582)^2}{241.7582} + \frac{(254-242.0)^2}{242}$

$\chi^2 = 35.177$

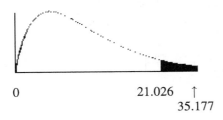

0          21.026   ↑
                    35.177

9. continued

Reject the null hypothesis. There is enough evidence to support the claim that the type of pet is dependent upon the income of the owner.

11.

$H_0$: The composition of the House of Representatives is independent of the state.

$H_1$: The composition of the House of Representatives is dependent upon the state. (claim)

C. V. = 7.815     d. f. = 3     $\alpha = 0.05$

$E = \frac{\text{(row sum)(column sum)}}{\text{grand total}}$

$E_{1,1} = \frac{(203)(320)}{542} = 119.8524$

$E_{1,2} = \frac{(203)(222)}{542} = 83.1476$

$E_{2,1} = \frac{(98)(320)}{542} = 57.8598$

$E_{2,2} = \frac{(98)(222)}{542} = 40.1402$

$E_{3,1} = \frac{(100)(320)}{542} = 59.0406$

$E_{3,2} = \frac{(100)(222)}{542} 40.9594$

$E_{4,1} = \frac{(141)(320)}{542} = 83.2472$

$E_{4,2} = \frac{(141)(222)}{542} = 57.7528$

| State | Democrats | Republicans |
|---|---|---|
| PA | 100(119.8524) | 103(83.1476) |
| OH | 39(57.8598) | 59(40.1402) |
| WV | 75(59.0406) | 25(40.9594) |
| MD | 106(83.2472) | 35(57.7528) |

$\chi^2 = \sum \frac{(O-E)^2}{E} = \frac{(100-119.8524)^2}{119.8524} + \frac{(103-83.1476)^2}{83.1476}$

$+ \frac{(39-57.8598)^2}{57.8598} + \frac{(59-40.1402)^2}{40.1402} + \frac{(75-59.0406)^2}{59.0406}$

$+ \frac{(25-40.9594)^2}{40.9594} + \frac{(106-83.2472)^2}{83.2472} + \frac{(35-57.7528)^2}{57.7528}$

$\chi^2 = 48.7521$

## 11. continued

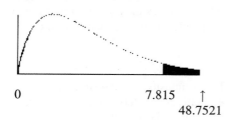

0                   7.815    ↑
                          48.7521

Reject the null hypothesis. There is enough evidence to support the claim that the composition of the legislature is dependent upon the state.

## 13.
$H_0$: The number of ads people think they've seen or heard in the media is independent of the gender of the individual.
$H_1$: The number of ads people think they've seen or heard in the media is dependent upon the gender of the individual. (claim)
C. V. = 13.277    d. f. = 4    $\alpha = 0.01$

$E_{1,1} = \frac{(300)(95)}{510} = 55.882$

$E_{1,2} = \frac{(300)(110)}{510} = 64.706$

$E_{1,3} = \frac{(300)(144)}{510} = 84.706$

$E_{1,4} = \frac{(300)(84)}{510} = 49.412$

$E_{1,5} = \frac{(300)(77)}{510} = 45.294$

$E_{2,1} = \frac{(210)(95)}{510} = 39.118$

$E_{2,2} = \frac{(210)(110)}{510} = 45.294$

$E_{2,3} = \frac{(210)(144)}{510} = 59.294$

$E_{2,4} = \frac{(210)(84)}{510} = 34.588$

$E_{2,5} = \frac{(210)(77)}{510} = 31.706$

| Gender | 1 - 30 | 31 - 50 | 51 - 100 |
|--------|--------|---------|----------|
| Men | 45(55.882) | 60(64.706) | 90(84.706) |
| Women | 50(39.118) | 50(45.294) | 54(59.294) |
| Total | 95 | 110 | 144 |

| Gender | 101 - 300 | 301 or more | Total |
|--------|-----------|-------------|-------|
| Men | 54(49.412) | 51(45.294) | 300 |
| Women | 30(34.588) | 26(31.706) | 210 |
| Total | 84 | 77 | 510 |

## 13. continued

$$\chi^2 = \sum \frac{(O-E)^2}{E} = \frac{(45-55.882)^2}{55.882} + \frac{(60-64.706)^2}{64.706}$$

$$+ \frac{(90-84.706)^2}{84.706} + \frac{(54-49.412)^2}{49.412} + \frac{(51-45.294)^2}{45.294}$$

$$+ \frac{(50-39.118)^2}{39.118} + \frac{(50-45.294)^2}{45.294} + \frac{(54-59.294)^2}{59.294}$$

$$+ \frac{(30-34.588)^2}{34.588} + \frac{(26-31.706)^2}{31.706} = 9.562$$

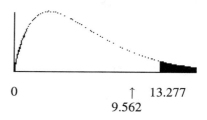

0                    ↑    13.277
                     9.562

Do not reject the null hypothesis. There is not enough evidence to support the claim that the number of ads people think they've seen or heard is related to the gender of the individual.

## 15.
$H_0$: The type of practice of an attorney is independent of the gender of the attorney. (claim)
$H_1$: The type of practice of an attorney is dependent upon the gender of the attorney.
C. V. = 5.991    d. f. = 2    $\alpha = 0.05$

$E_{1,1} = \frac{(176)(140)}{240} = 102.667$

$E_{1,2} = \frac{(34)(140)}{240} = 19.833$

$E_{1,3} = \frac{(30)(140)}{240} = 17.5$

$E_{2,1} = \frac{(176)(100)}{240} = 73.333$

$E_{2,2} = \frac{(34)(100)}{240} = 14.167$

$E_{2,3} = \frac{(30)(100)}{240} = 12.5$

| Gender | Private Practice | Law Firm |
|--------|------------------|----------|
| Male | 112(102.667) | 16(19.833) |
| Female | 64(73.333) | 18(14.167) |

| Gender | Government |
|--------|------------|
| Male | 12(17.5) |
| Female | 18(12.5) |

15. continued

$$\chi^2 = \sum \frac{(O-E)^2}{E} = \frac{(112-102.667)^2}{102.667} + \frac{(16-19.833)^2}{19.833}$$

$$+ \frac{(12-17.5)^2}{17.5} + \frac{(64-73.333)^2}{73.333} + \frac{(18-14.167)^2}{14.167}$$

$$+ \frac{(18-12.5)^2}{12.5} = 7.963$$

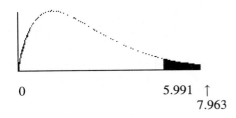

0         5.991 ↑
              7.963

Reject the null hypothesis. There is enough evidence to reject the claim that the type of practice is independent of the gender of the attorney.

17.
$H_0$: The type of video rented by a person is independent of the person's age.
$H_1$: The type of video a person rents is dependent on the person's age. (claim)
C. V. = 13.362   d. f. = 8   $\alpha = 0.10$

| Age | Doc. | Comedy | Mystery |
|---|---|---|---|
| 12-20 | 14(6.588) | 9(13.433) | 8(10.979) |
| 21-29 | 15(8.075) | 14(16.467) | 9(13.458) |
| 30-38 | 9(14.663) | 21(29.9) | 39(24.438) |
| 39-47 | 7(9.775) | 22(19.933) | 17(16.292) |
| 48 + | 6(11.9) | 38(24.267) | 12(19.833) |

$$\chi^2 = \frac{(14-6.588)^2}{6.588} + \frac{(9-13.433)^2}{13.433} + \frac{(8-10.979)^2}{10.979}$$

$$+ \frac{(15-8.075)^2}{8.075} + \frac{(14-16.467)^2}{16.467} + \frac{(9-13.458)^2}{13.458}$$

$$+ \frac{(9-14.663)^2}{14.663} + \frac{(21-29.9)^2}{29.9} + \frac{(39-24.438)^2}{24.438}$$

$$+ \frac{(7-9.775)^2}{9.775} + \frac{(22-19.933)^2}{19.933} + \frac{(17-16.292)^2}{16.292}$$

$$+ \frac{(6-11.9)^2}{11.9} + \frac{(38-24.267)^2}{24.267} + \frac{(12-19.833)^2}{19.833}$$

$$\chi^2 = 46.733$$

17. continued

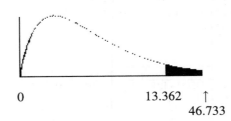

0        13.362 ↑
           46.733

Reject the null hypothesis. There is enough evidence to support the claim that the type of movie selected is related to the age of the customer.

19.
$H_0$: The type of snack purchased is independent of the gender of the consumer. (claim)
$H_1$: The type of snack purchased is dependent upon the gender of the consumer.
C. V. = 4.605    d. f. = 2

| Gender | Hot Dog | Peanuts | Popcorn | Total |
|---|---|---|---|---|
| Male | 12(13.265) | 21(15.388) | 19(23.347) | 52 |
| Female | 13(11.735) | 8(13.612) | 25(20.653) | 46 |
| Total | 25 | 29 | 44 | 98 |

$$\chi^2 = \sum \frac{(O-E)^2}{E} = \frac{(12-13.265)^2}{13.265} + \frac{(21-15.388)^2}{15.388}$$

$$+ \frac{(19-23.347)^2}{23.347} + \frac{(13-11.735)^2}{11.735} + \frac{(8-13.612)^2}{13.612}$$

$$+ \frac{(25-20.653)^2}{20.653} = 6.342$$

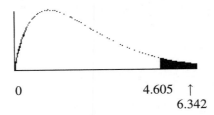

0        4.605 ↑
          6.342

Reject the null hypothesis. There is enough evidence to reject the claim that the type of snack chosen is independent of the gender of the individual.

21.
$H_0$: The type of book purchased by the individual is independent of the gender of the individual. (claim)

21. continued
$H_1$: The type of book purchased by the individual is dependent on the gender of the individual.
$\alpha = 0.05$    d. f. = 2

| Gender | Mystery | Romance | Self-help | Total |
|--------|---------|---------|-----------|-------|
| Male | 243(214.121) | 201(198.260) | 191(222.618) | 635 |
| Female | 135(163.879) | 149(151.740) | 202(170.382) | 486 |
| Total | 378 | 350 | 393 | 1121 |

$$\chi^2 = \sum \frac{(O-E)^2}{E} = \frac{(243-214.121)^2}{214.121} + \frac{(201-198.260)^2}{198.260}$$

$$+ \frac{(191-222.618)^2}{222.618} + \frac{(135-163.879)^2}{163.879}$$

$$+ \frac{(149-151.740)^2}{151.740} + \frac{(202-170.382)^2}{170.382} = 19.429$$

P-value < 0.005  (0.00006)
Reject the null hypothesis since P-value < 0.05. There is enough evidence to reject the claim that the type of book purchased is independent of gender.

23.
$H_0$: $p_1 = p_2 = p_3 = p_4$  (claim)
$H_1$: At least one proportion is different.

C. V. = 7.815    d. f. = 3

$$E(passed) = \frac{120(167)}{120} = 41.75$$

$$E(failed) = \frac{120(313)}{120} = 78.25$$

| | Southside | West End | East Hills | Jefferson |
|--------|-----------|----------|------------|-----------|
| Passed | 49(41.75) | 38(41.75) | 46(41.75) | 34(41.75) |
| Failed | 71(78.25) | 82(78.25) | 74(78.25) | 86(78.25) |

$$\chi^2 = \frac{(49-41.75)^2}{41.75} + \frac{(38-41.75)^2}{41.75} + \frac{(46-41.75)^2}{41.75}$$

$$+ \frac{(34-41.75)^2}{41.75} + \frac{(71-78.25)^2}{78.25} + \frac{(82-78.25)^2}{78.25}$$

$$+ \frac{(74-78.25)^2}{78.25} + \frac{(86-78.25)^2}{78.25} = 5.317$$

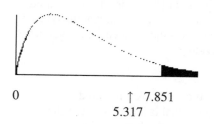

0                        ↑  7.851
                        5.317

23. continued
Do not reject the null hypothesis. There is not enough evidence to reject the claim that the proportions are equal.

25.
$H_0$: $p_1 = p_2 = p_3 = p_4$   (claim)
$H_1$: At least one proportion is different.
C. V. = 7.815    d. f. = 3

| | Services | Manufacturing | Government | Other |
|--------------|----------|---------------|------------|-------|
| 10 years ago | 33(30.6) | 13(15) | 11(11.4) | 3(3) |
| Now | 18(20.4) | 12(10) | 8(7.6) | 2(2) |
| Total | 51 | 25 | 19 | 5 |

$$\chi^2 = \frac{(33-30.6)^2}{30.6} + \frac{(13-15)^2}{15} + \frac{(11-11.4)^2}{11.4} +$$

$$\frac{(3-3)^2}{3} + \frac{(18-20.4)^2}{20.4} + \frac{(12-10)^2}{10} + \frac{(8-7.6)^2}{7.6}$$

$$+ \frac{(2-2)^2}{2} = 1.172$$

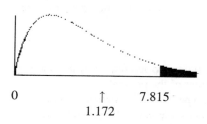

0                 ↑        7.815
                1.172

Do not reject the null hypothesis. There is not enough evidence to reject the claim that the proportions are the same. Since the survey was done in Pennsylvania, it is doubtful that it can be generalized to the population of the United States.

27.
$H_0$: $p_1 = p_2 = p_3 = p_4$   (claim)
$H_1$: At least one proportion is different.
C. V. = 6.251    d. f. = 3

$$E(yes) = \frac{(100)(132)}{400} = 33$$

$$E(no) = \frac{(100)(268)}{400} = 67$$

| | North | South | East | West |
|-----|-------|-------|------|------|
| Yes | 43(33) | 39(33) | 22(33) | 28(33) |
| No | 57(67) | 61(67) | 78(67) | 72(67) |

$$\chi^2 = \frac{(43-33)^2}{33} + \frac{(39-33)^2}{33} + \frac{(22-33)^2}{33} +$$

$$\frac{(28-33)^2}{33} + \frac{(57-67)^2}{67} + \frac{(61-67)^2}{67} + \frac{(78-67)^2}{67}$$

$$+ \frac{(72-67)^2}{67} = 12.755$$

27. continued

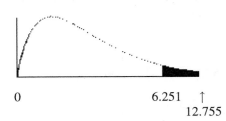

0          6.251    ↑
                    12.755

Reject the null hypothesis. There is enough evidence to reject the claim that the proportions are the same.

29.
$H_0$: $p_1 = p_2 = p_3 = p_4$   (claim)
$H_1$: At least one proportion is different.
$\alpha = 0.05$    d. f. = 3

$E(\text{on bars}) = \frac{30(62)}{120} = 15.5$

$E(\text{not on bars}) = \frac{30(58)}{120} = 14.5$

|     | N | S | E | W |
|-----|---|---|---|---|
| on  | 15(15.5) | 18(15.5) | 13(15.5) | 16(15.5) |
| off | 15(14.5) | 12(14.5) | 17(14.5) | 14(14.5) |

$\chi^2 = \frac{(15-15.5)^2}{15.5} + \frac{(18-15.5)^2}{15.5} + \frac{(13-15.5)^2}{15.5} +$

$\frac{(16-15.5)^2}{15.5} + \frac{(15-14.5)^2}{14.5} + \frac{(12-14.5)^2}{14.5} +$

$\frac{(17-14.5)^2}{14.5} + \frac{(14-14.5)^2}{14.5} = 1.734$

P-value > 0.10  (0.629)
Do not reject the null hypothesis. There is not enough evidence to reject the claim that the proportions are the same.

31.
$H_0$: $p_1 = p_2 = p_3$  (claim)
$H_1$: At least one proportion is different.
C. V. = 4.605    d. f. = 2

$E(\text{list}) = \frac{96(219)}{288} = 73$

$E(\text{no list}) = \frac{96(69)}{288} = 23$

|         | A | B | C |
|---------|---|---|---|
| list    | 77(73) | 74(73) | 68(73) |
| no list | 19(23) | 22((23) | 28(23) |

31. continued

$\chi^2 = \frac{(77-73)^2}{73} + \frac{(74-73)^2}{73} + \frac{(68-73)^2}{73}$

$+ \frac{(19-23)^2}{23} + \frac{(22-23)^2}{23} + \frac{(28-23)^2}{23}$

$\chi^2 = 2.401$

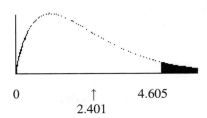

0          ↑          4.605
          2.401

Do not reject the null hypothesis. There is not enough evidence to reject the claim that the proportions are the same.

33.
$\chi^2 = \frac{(|O-E|-0.5)^2}{E} = \frac{(|12-9.6|-0.5)^2}{9.6}$

$+ \frac{(|15-17.4|-0.5)^2}{17.4} + \frac{(|9-11.4|-0.5)^2}{11.4}$

$+ \frac{(|23-20.6|-0.5)^2}{20.6}$

$= \frac{3.61}{9.6} + \frac{3.61}{17.4} + \frac{3.61}{11.4} + \frac{3.61}{20.6}$

$= 0.376 + 0.207 + 0.317 + 0.175 = 1.075$

EXERCISE SET 11-4

1.
The analysis of variance using the F-test can be used to compare 3 or more means.

3.
The populations from which the samples were obtained must be normally distributed. The samples must be independent of each other. The variances of the populations must be equal.

5.
$F = \frac{s_B^2}{s_W^2}$

7.
One.

# Chapter 11 - Other Chi-Square Tests

**9.**

$H_0$: $\mu_1 = \mu_2 = \mu_3$

$H_1$: At least one mean is different from the others. (claim)

C. V. = 3.47 $\qquad \alpha = 0.05$

d. f. N. = 2 $\qquad$ d. f. D. = 21

$\overline{X}_{GM} = 4.554$ $\quad s_B^2 = 9.82113$ $\quad s_W^2 = 4.93225$

$$F = \frac{9.82113}{4.93225} = 1.9912$$

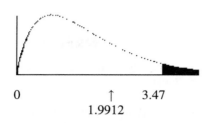

0 $\qquad\qquad \uparrow \qquad$ 3.47
$\qquad\qquad$ 1.9912

Do not reject the null hypothesis. There is not enough evidence to support the claim that at least one mean is different from the others.

**11.**

$H_0$: $\mu_1 = \mu_2 = \mu_3$

$H_1$: At least one mean is different from the others. (claim)

C. V. = 3.98 $\qquad \alpha = 0.05$

d. f. N = 2 $\qquad$ d. f. D = 11

$\overline{X}_{GM} = \frac{52414}{14} = 3743.857$

$s_B^2 = 3,633,540.88$

$s_W^2 = 1,330,350$

$$F = \frac{3633540.88}{1330350} = 2.7313$$

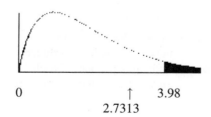

0 $\qquad\qquad \uparrow \qquad$ 3.98
$\qquad\qquad$ 2.7313

Do not reject the null hypothesis. There is not enough evidence to support the claim that at least one mean is different from the others.

**13.**

$H_0$: $\mu_1 = \mu_2 = \mu_3$

$H_1$: At least one mean is different. (claim)

**13. continued**

k = 3 $\quad$ N = 18 $\quad$ d.f.N. = 2 $\quad$ d.f.D. = 15

CV = 3.68

$\overline{X}_1 = 7$ $\qquad\qquad s_1^2 = 1.37$

$\overline{X}_2 = 8.12$ $\qquad\quad s_2^2 = 0.64$

$\overline{X}_3 = 5.23$ $\qquad\quad s_3^2 = 2.66$

$\overline{X}_{GM} = 6.7833$

$$s_B^2 = \frac{6(7-6.78)^2}{2} + \frac{6(8.12-6.78)^2}{2}$$

$$+ \frac{6(5.23-6.78)^2}{2} = 12.7$$

$$s_W^2 = \frac{5(1.37)+5(0.64)+5(2.66)}{5+5+5}$$

$$s_W^2 = \frac{23.35}{15} = 1.56$$

$$F = \frac{12.7}{1.56} = 8.14$$

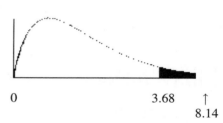

0 $\qquad\qquad$ 3.68 $\quad \uparrow$
$\qquad\qquad\qquad\qquad$ 8.14

Reject the null hypothesis. There is enough evidence to support the claim that at least one mean is different.

**15.**

$H_0$: $\mu_1 = \mu_2 = \mu_3$ (claim)

$H_1$: At least one mean is different from the others.

C. V. = 4.10 $\qquad \alpha = 0.10$

d. f. N = 2 $\qquad$ d. f. D = 10

$\overline{X}_1 = 35.4$ $\qquad\quad s_1^2 = 351.8$

$\overline{X}_2 = 68.75$ $\qquad s_2^2 = 338.25$

$\overline{X}_3 = 44.25$ $\qquad s_3^2 = 277.583$

$\overline{X}_{GM} = \frac{629}{13} = 48.385$

$$s_B^2 = \frac{\sum n_i(\overline{X}_i - \overline{X}_{GM})^2}{k-1}$$

$$s_B^2 = \frac{5(35.4-48.385)^2}{2} + \frac{4(68.75-48.385)^2}{2}$$

$$+ \frac{4(44.25-48.385)^2}{2} = 1285.188$$

118

**15. continued**

$$s_W^2 = \frac{\sum (n_i - 1)s_i^2}{\sum (n_i - 1)}$$

$$= \frac{4(351.8) + 3(338.25) + 3(277.583)}{4 + 3 + 3}$$

$$= 325.47$$

$$F = \frac{s_B^2}{s_W^2} = \frac{1285.188}{325.47} = 3.9487$$

Do not reject the null hypothesis. There is not enough evidence to reject the claim that the means are the same.

**17.**
$H_0$: $\mu_1 = \mu_2 = \mu_3$
$H_1$: At least one mean is different from the others. (claim)
$\alpha = 0.10$
d. f. N = 2    d. f. D = 19

$\overline{X}_1 = 233.33$    $s_1 = 28.225$
$\overline{X}_2 = 203.125$    $s_2 = 39.364$
$\overline{X}_3 = 155.625$    $s_3 = 28.213$

$\overline{X}_{GM} = 194.091$

$$s_B^2 = \frac{21,729.735}{2} = 10,864.8675$$

$$s_W^2 = \frac{20,402.083}{19} = 1073.794$$

$$F = \frac{s_B^2}{s_W^2} = \frac{10,864.8675}{1073.794} = 10.12$$

P-value = 0.00102
Reject since P-value < 0.10.
The is enough evidence to support the claim that at least one mean is different from the others.

**19.**
$H_0$: $\mu_1 = \mu_2 = \mu_3 = \mu_4$
$H_1$: At least one mean is different. (claim)
C. V. = 5.29    $\alpha = 0.01$
d. f. N = 3    d. f. D = 16

$\overline{X}_{GM} = \frac{42}{20} = 2.1$

$$s_B^2 = \frac{10.2}{3} = 3.4$$

$$s_W^2 = \frac{85.6193}{16} = 5.35$$

$$F = \frac{3.4}{5.35} = 0.636$$

**19. continued**

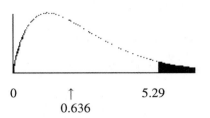

Do not reject the null hypothesis. There is not enough evidence to support the claim that at least one mean is different. Students may have had discipline problems. Parents may not like the regular school district, etc.

## REVIEW EXERCISES - CHAPTER 11

**1.**
$H_0$: The number of sales is equally distributed over five regions. (claim)
$H_1$: The null hypothesis is not true.

C. V. = 9.488    d. f. = 4
$E = \frac{1328}{5} = 265.6$

$$\chi^2 = \sum \frac{(O-E)^2}{E} = \frac{(236-265.6)^2}{265.6}$$

$$+ \frac{(324-265.6)^2}{265.6} + \frac{(182-265.6)^2}{265.6}$$

$$+ \frac{(221-265.6)^2}{265.6} + \frac{(365-265.6)^2}{265.6} = 87.14$$

Alternate Solution:

| O | E | O − E | $(O-E)^2$ | $\frac{(O-E)^2}{E}$ |
|---|---|---|---|---|
| 236 | 265.6 | -29.6 | 876.18 | 3.299 |
| 324 | 265.6 | 58.4 | 3410.56 | 12.841 |
| 182 | 265.6 | -83.6 | 6988.96 | 26.314 |
| 221 | 265.6 | -44.6 | 1989.16 | 7.489 |
| 365 | 265.6 | 99.4 | 9880.36 | 37.200 |
| | | | | 87.143 |

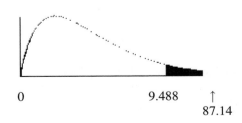

Reject the null hypothesis. There is enough evidence to reject the claim that the number of items sold in each region is the same.

3.

$H_0$: The gender of the individual is not related to whether or not a person would use the labels.

$H_1$: The gender is related to use of the labels. (claim)

C. V. $= 4.605$    d. f. $= 2$

| Gender | Yes | No | Undecided |
|--------|-----|-----|-----------|
| Men | 114(120.968) | 30(22.258) | 6(6.774) |
| Women | 136(129.032) | 16(23.742) | 8(7.226) |

$$\chi^2 = \frac{(114-120.968)^2}{120.968} + \frac{(30-22.258)^2}{22.258} + \frac{(6-6.774)^2}{6.774}$$

$$+ \frac{(136-129.032)^2}{129.032} + \frac{(16-23.742)^2}{23.742} + \frac{(8-7.226)^2}{7.226}$$

$$\chi^2 = 6.16$$

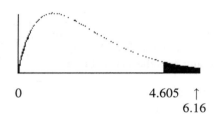

0                                   4.605 ↑
                                            6.16

Reject the null hypothesis. There is enough evidence to support the claim that opinion is dependent on gender.

5.

$H_0$: The type of investment is independent of the age of the investor.

$H_1$: The type of investment is dependent upon the age of the investor. (claim)

C. V. $= 9.488$    d. f. $= 4$

| Age | Large | Small | Inter. |
|-----|-------|-------|--------|
| 45 | 20(28.18) | 10(15.45) | 10(15.45) |
| 65 | 42(33.82) | 24(18.55) | 24(18.55) |

| Age | CD | Bond |
|-----|-----|------|
| 45 | 15(9.55) | 45(31.36) |
| 65 | 6(11.45) | 24(37.64) |

$$\chi^2 = \frac{(20-28.18)^2}{28.18} + \frac{(10-15.45)^2}{15.45} + \frac{(10-15.45)^2}{15.45}$$

$$+ \frac{(15-9.55)^2}{9.55} + \frac{(45-31.36)^2}{31.36} + \frac{(42-33.82)^2}{33.82} +$$

$$\frac{(24-18.55)^2}{18.55} + \frac{(24-18.55)^2}{18.55} + \frac{(6-11.45)^2}{11.45} +$$

$$\frac{(24-37.64)^2}{37.64} = 28.0$$

5. continued

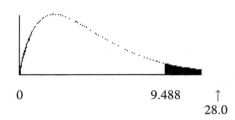

0                          9.488    ↑
                                        28.0

Reject the null hypothesis. There is enough evidence to support the claim that the type of investment is dependent on age.

7.

$H_0$: $p_1 = p_2 = p_3$  (claim)

$H_1$: At least one proportion is different.

$\alpha = 0.01$    d. f. $= 2$

C. V. $= 9.210$

$E(\text{work}) = \frac{80(114)}{240} = 38$

$E(\text{don't work}) = \frac{80(126)}{240} = 42$

| | 16 | 17 | 18 |
|--------------|-------|-------|-------|
| work | 45(38) | 31(38) | 38(38) |
| don't work | 35(42) | 49(42) | 42(42) |

$$\chi^2 = \frac{(45-38)^2}{38} + \frac{(31-38)^2}{38} + \frac{(38-38)^2}{38}$$

$$+ \frac{(35-42)^2}{42} + \frac{(49-42)^2}{42} + \frac{(42-42)^2}{42} = 4.912$$

Do not reject the null hypothesis. There is not enough evidence to reject the claim that the proportions are the same.

9.

$H_0$: $p_1 = p_2 = p_3 = p_4$

$H_1$: At least one proportion is different.

C. V. $= 6.251$    d. f. $= 3$

$E(\text{yes}) = \frac{50(58)}{200} = 14.5$

$E(\text{no}) = \frac{50(142)}{200} = 35.5$

| | A | B | C | D |
|-----|-------|-------|-------|-------|
| Yes | 12(14.5) | 15(14.5) | 10(14.5) | 21(14.5) |
| No | 38(35.5) | 35(35.5) | 40(35.5) | 29(35.5) |

$$\chi^2 = \frac{(12-14.5)^2}{14.5} + \frac{(15-14.5)^2}{14.5} + \frac{(10-14.5)^2}{14.5} +$$

$$\frac{(21-14.5)^2}{14.5} + \frac{(38-35.5)^2}{35.5} + \frac{(35-35.5)^2}{35.5}$$

$$+ \frac{(40-35.5)^2}{35.5} + \frac{(29-35.5)^2}{35.5} = 6.70$$

## 9. continued

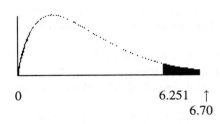

0          6.251 ↑
                     6.70

Reject the null hypothesis. There is enough
evidence to reject the claim that the
proportions are the same.

## 11.

$H_0$: $\mu_1 = \mu_2 = \mu_3$   (claim)
$H_1$: At least one mean is different from the
      others.
C. V. = 6.01     $\alpha = 0.01$
d. f. N = 2     d. f. D = 18

$\overline{X}_1 = 197.57$      $s_1^2 = 373.62$

$\overline{X}_2 = 295.57$      $s_2^2 = 6639.29$

$\overline{X}_3 = 103.14$      $s_3^2 = 181.48$

$\overline{X}_{GM} = \frac{4174}{21} = 198.76$

$s_B^2 = \frac{\sum n_i(\overline{X}_i - \overline{X}_{GM})^2}{k-1}$

$= \frac{7(197.57-198.76)^2 + 7(295.57-198.76)^2}{3-1}$

$+ \frac{7(103.14-198.76)^2}{3-1} = 64808.72$

$s_W^2 = \frac{\sum(n_i-1)s_i^2}{\sum(n_i-1)}$

$= \frac{6(373.62) + 6(6639.29) + 6(181.48)}{6+6+6} = 2398.13$

$F = \frac{s_B^2}{s_W^2} = \frac{64808.72}{2398.13} = 27.02$

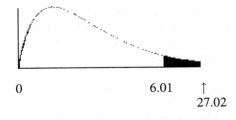

0           6.01    ↑
                       27.02

Reject. At least one mean is different from
the others.

## 13.

$H_0$: $\mu_1 = \mu_2 = \mu_3 = \mu_4$     (claim)
$H_1$: At least one mean is different from the
      others.
C. V. = 3.86      $\alpha = 0.05$
d. f. N = 3     d. f. D = 9

$\overline{X}_1 = 7$            $s_1 = 0.816$

$\overline{X}_2 = 6.333$       $s_2 = 0.578$

$\overline{X}_3 = 11.667$      $s_3 = 0.577$

$\overline{X}_4 = 7.333$       $s_4 = 1.528$

$\overline{X}_{GM} = 8$

$s_B^2 = \frac{\sum n_i(\overline{X}_i - \overline{X}_{GM})^2}{k-1}$

$s_B^2 = \frac{4(7-8)^2}{3} + \frac{3(6.333-8)^2}{3} + \frac{3(11.667-8)^2}{3}$

$+ \frac{3(7.333-8)^2}{3} = \frac{54.01}{3} = 18.0$

$s_W^2 = \frac{\sum(n_i-1)s_i^2}{\sum(n_i-1)}$

$s_W^2 = \frac{3(0.816)^2 + 2(0.578)^2 + 2(0.577)^2 + 2(1.528)^2}{3+2+2+2}$

$s_W^2 = 0.889$

$F = \frac{s_B^2}{s_W^2} = \frac{18.0}{0.889} = 20.25$

Reject. At least one mean is different from
the others.

## 15.

$H_0$: $\mu_1 = \mu_2 = \mu_3$
$H_1$: At least one mean is different.
C. V. = 3.89     $\alpha = 0.05$
d. f. N = 2     d. f. D = 12

$F = \frac{4300.8}{65.9} = 65.263$

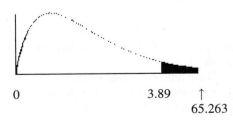

0           3.89    ↑
                     65.263

Reject. At least one mean is different from
the others.

17.
$H_0$: $\mu_1 = \mu_2 = \mu_3 = \mu_4$
$H_1$: At least one mean is different from the others.
C. V. = 3.10    $\alpha = 0.05$
d. f. N = 3    d. f. D = 20

$$F = \frac{20.264}{12.7585} = 1.59$$

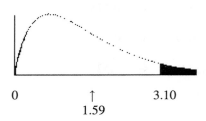

0                    ↑              3.10
                   1.59

Do not reject the null hypothesis. There is not enough evidence to conclude that there is a difference in the means.

CHAPTER 11 QUIZ

1. False, it is one-tailed right.
2. True
3. False, there is little agreement between observed and expected frequencies.
4. False, there could be a significant difference between only some of the means.
5. False, degrees of freedom are used to find the critical value.
6. False, the null hypothesis should not be rejected.
7. c
8. b
9. d
10. d
11. a
12. a
13. 6
14. Independent
15. Right
16. At least five
17. ANOVA

18. $H_0$: The number of advertisements is equally distributed over five geographic regions.
$H_1$: The number of advertisements is not equally distributed over five regions.
C. V. = 9.488    d. f. = 4    E = 240.4
$\chi^2 = \sum \frac{(O-E)^2}{E} = 45.4$

18. continued
Reject the null hypothesis. There is enough evidence to reject the claim that the number of advertisements is equally distributed.

19. $H_0$: The ads produced the same number of responses. (claim)
$H_1$: The ads produced different numbers of responses.
C. V. = 13.277    d. f. = 4    E = 64.6
$\chi^2 = \sum \frac{(O-E)^2}{E} = 12.6$
Do not reject the null hypothesis. There is not enough evidence to reject the claim that the ads produced the same number of responses.

20. $H_0$: 48% of the customers order hamburgers, 33% order chicken, 19% order salad. (claim)
$H_1$: The distribution is not the same as stated in the null hypothesis.
C. V. = 5.991    d. f. = 2
$\chi^2 = 4.6$
Do not reject the null hypothesis. There is not enough evidence to reject the manager's claim.

21. $H_0$: Each gift was purchased with the same frequency.  (claim)
$H_1$: The gifts were not purchased with the same frequency.
C. V. = 9.21    d. f. = 2
$\chi^2 = 73.1$
Reject the null hypothesis. There is enough evidence to reject the claim that the gifts were purchased with the same frequency.

22. $H_0$: The type of novel purchased is independent of the gender of the purchaser. (claim)
$H_1$: The type of novel purchased is dependent on the gender of the purchaser.
C. V. = 5.991    d. f. = 2
$\chi^2 = 132.9$
Reject the null hypothesis. There is enough evidence to reject the claim that the novel purchased is independent of the gender of the purchaser.

23. $H_0$: The type of pizza ordered is independent of the age of the purchaser.
$H_1$: The type of pizza ordered is dependent on the age of the purchaser. (claim)
C. V. = 14.684    d. f. = 9

23. continued
$\chi^2 = 107.3$
Reject the null hypothesis. There is enough
evidence to support the claim that the type of
pizza ordered is related to the age of the
purchaser.

24. $H_0$: The color of the pennant purchased
is independent of the gender of the
purchaser. (claim)
$H_1$: The color of the pennant purchased is
dependent on the gender of the purchaser.
C. V. = 4.605    d. f. = 2
$\chi^2 = 5.6$
Reject the null hypothesis. There is enough
evidence to reject the claim that the color of
the pennant purchased is independent of the
gender of the purchaser.

25. $H_0$: $\mu_1 = \mu_2 = \mu_3$ (claim)
$H_1$: At least one mean is different from the
others.
C. V. = 3.55
$s_B^2 = 785.333$    $s_W^2 = 6607.238$
$F = \frac{785.333}{6607.238} = 0.119$
Do not reject. There is not enough evidence
to say there is a difference in the means.

26. $H_0$: $\mu_1 = \mu_2 = \mu_3 = \mu_4$ (claim)
$H_1$: At least one mean is different from the
others.
C. V. = 3.10
$s_B^2 = 42.37$    $s_W^2 = 10.125$
$F = \frac{42.37}{10.125} = 4.185$
Reject $H_0$. At least one mean is different
from the others.

27. $H_0$: $\mu_1 = \mu_2 = \mu_3$
$H_1$: At least one mean is different from the
others. (claim)
C. V. = 6.36    $\alpha = 0.01$
$s_B^2 = 4.936$    $s_W^2 = 6.975$
$F = 0.71$
Do not reject $H_0$. There is not enough
evidence to show there is a difference in the
means.

28. $H_0$: $\mu_1 = \mu_2 = \mu_3$
$H_1$: At least one mean is different from the
others. (claim)
C. V. = 3.63    $\alpha = 0.05$
$s_B^2 = 13.379$    $s_W^2 = 271.486$
$F = 0.049$

28. continued
Do not reject $H_0$. There is not enough
evidence to say there is a difference in the
means.

29. $H_0$: $\mu_1 = \mu_2 = \mu_3$
$H_1$: At least one mean is different from the
others. (claim)
C. V. = 3.89    $\alpha = 0.05$
$s_B^2 = 3913.87$    $s_W^2 = 78.767$
F = 49.689
Reject $H_0$. At least one mean is different
from the others.

# Appendix A - Algebra Review

A-1

A-1. $9! = 9 \cdot 8 \cdot 7 \cdot 6 \cdot 5 \cdot 4 \cdot 3 \cdot 2 \cdot 1 = 362,880$

A-3. $5! = 5 \cdot 4 \cdot 3 \cdot 2 \cdot 1 = 120$

A-5. $1! = 1$

A-7. $\frac{12!}{9!} = \frac{12 \cdot 11 \cdot 10 \cdot 9!}{9!} = 1320$

A-9. $\frac{5!}{3!} = \frac{5 \cdot 4 \cdot 3!}{3!} = 20$

A-11. $\frac{9!}{(4!)(5!)} = \frac{9 \cdot 8 \cdot 7 \cdot 6 \cdot 5!}{4 \cdot 3 \cdot 2 \cdot 1 \cdot 5!} = 126$

A-13. $\frac{8!}{4!4!} = \frac{8 \cdot 7 \cdot 6 \cdot 5 \cdot 4!}{4 \cdot 3 \cdot 2 \cdot 1 \cdot 4!} = 70$

A-15. $\frac{10!}{(10!)(0!)} = \frac{10!}{10! \cdot 1} = 1$

A-17. $\frac{8!}{3!3!2!} = \frac{8 \cdot 7 \cdot 6 \cdot 5 \cdot 4 \cdot 3!}{3! \cdot 3 \cdot 2 \cdot 1 \cdot 2 \cdot 1} = 560$

A-19. $\frac{10!}{3!2!5!} = \frac{10 \cdot 9 \cdot 8 \cdot 7 \cdot 6 \cdot 5!}{3 \cdot 2 \cdot 1 \cdot 2 \cdot 1 \cdot 5!} = 2520$

A-2

A-21.

| X | $X^2$ | $X - \overline{X}$ | $(X - \overline{X})^2$ |
|---|---|---|---|
| 9 | 81 | − 3.1 | 9.61 |
| 17 | 289 | 4.9 | 24.01 |
| 32 | 1024 | 19.9 | 396.01 |
| 16 | 256 | 3.9 | 15.21 |
| 8 | 64 | − 4.1 | 16.81 |
| 2 | 4 | − 10.1 | 102.01 |
| 9 | 81 | − 3.1 | 9.61 |
| 7 | 49 | − 5.1 | 26.01 |
| 3 | 9 | − 9.1 | 82.81 |
| 18 | 324 | 5.9 | 34.81 |
| 121 | 2181 | | 716.9 |

$\sum X = 121$   $\overline{X} = \frac{121}{10} = 12.1$   $\sum X^2 = 2181$

$(\sum X)^2 = 121^2 = 14641$   $\sum(X-\overline{X})^2 = 716.9$

A-23.

| X | $X^2$ | $X - \overline{X}$ | $(X - \overline{X})^2$ |
|---|---|---|---|
| 5 | 25 | − 1.4 | 1.96 |
| 12 | 144 | 5.6 | 31.36 |
| 8 | 64 | 1.6 | 2.56 |
| 3 | 9 | − 3.4 | 11.56 |
| 4 | 16 | − 2.4 | 5.76 |
| 32 | 258 | | 53.20 |

$\sum X = 32$   $\overline{X} = \frac{32}{5} = 6.4$   $\sum X^2 = 258$

A-23. continued

$(\sum X)^2 = 32^2 = 1024$   $\sum(X-\overline{X})^2 = 53.2$

A-25.

| X | $X^2$ | $X - \overline{X}$ | $(X - \overline{X})^2$ |
|---|---|---|---|
| 80 | 6400 | 14.4 | 207.36 |
| 76 | 5776 | 10.4 | 108.16 |
| 42 | 1764 | − 23.6 | 556.96 |
| 53 | 2809 | − 12.6 | 158.76 |
| 77 | 5929 | 11.4 | 129.96 |
| 328 | 22678 | | 1161.20 |

$\sum X = 328$   $\overline{X} = \frac{328}{5} = 65.6$   $\sum X^2 = 22678$

$(\sum X)^2 = 328^2 = 107584$   $\sum(X-\overline{X})^2 = 1161.2$

A-27.

| X | $X^2$ | $X - \overline{X}$ | $(X - \overline{X})^2$ |
|---|---|---|---|
| 53 | 2809 | − 16.3 | 265.69 |
| 72 | 5184 | 2.7 | 7.29 |
| 81 | 6561 | 11.7 | 136.89 |
| 42 | 1764 | − 27.3 | 745.29 |
| 63 | 3969 | − 6.3 | 39.69 |
| 71 | 5041 | 1.7 | 2.89 |
| 73 | 5329 | 3.7 | 13.69 |
| 85 | 7225 | 15.7 | 246.49 |
| 98 | 9604 | 28.7 | 823.69 |
| 55 | 3025 | − 14.3 | 204.49 |
| 693 | 50511 | | 2486.10 |

$\sum X = 693$   $\overline{X} = \frac{693}{10} = 69.3$   $\sum X^2 = 50511$

$(\sum X)^2 = 693^2 = 480249$   $\sum(X-\overline{X})^2 = 2486.1$

A-29.

| X | $X^2$ | $X - \overline{X}$ | $(X - \overline{X})^2$ |
|---|---|---|---|
| 12 | 144 | − 41 | 1681 |
| 52 | 2704 | − 1 | 1 |
| 36 | 1296 | − 17 | 289 |
| 81 | 6561 | 28 | 784 |
| 63 | 3969 | 10 | 100 |
| 74 | 5476 | 21 | 441 |
| 318 | 20150 | | 3296 |

$\sum X = 318$   $\overline{X} = \frac{318}{6} = 53$   $\sum X^2 = 20150$

$(\sum X)^2 = 318^2 = 101124$   $\sum(X-\overline{X})^2 = 3296$

A-3

A-31.

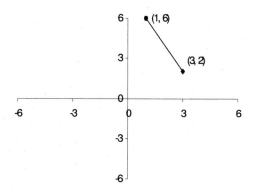

A-33.

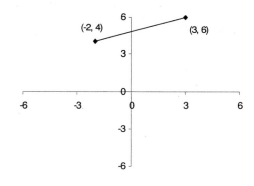

A-35.

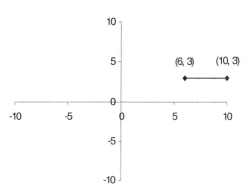

A-37.

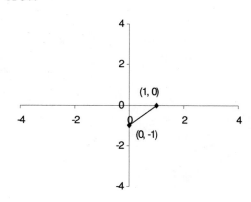

Two points are:  (1, 0) and (0, -1).

A-39.

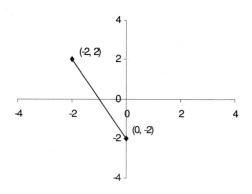

Two points are:  (-2, 2) and (0, -2).

# Notes

# Notes

# Notes

# Notes

# Notes

# Notes

# Notes